STO

ACPL ITEM

DISCARDED

ALLEN COUNTY PUBLIC LIBRARY
3 1833 00126 9940

D1474627

617.05
D83m
Drotar, David L.
Micro-surgery

2195960

*617.05 D83m   2195960
DROTAR, DAVID L.
MICRO-SURGERY :

ALLEN COUNTY PUBLIC LIBRARY

FORT WAYNE, INDIANA 46802

You may return this book to any agency, branch,
or bookmobile of the Allen County Public Library.

DEMCO

MICRO-SURGERY

Also by the author

FUN SCIENCE
POCKET CALCULATORS (with Arnold Madison)

MICRO-SURGERY

*Revolution in
the Operating Room*

David Lee Drotar

BEAUFORT BOOKS, INC.
New York / Toronto

ALLEN COUNTY PUBLIC LIBRARY
FORT WAYNE, INDIANA

Copyright © 1981 by David Lee Drotar
All rights reserved. No part of this publication may be reproduced or transmitted
in any form or by any means, electronic or mechanical, including photocopy,
recording, or any information storage and retrieval system now known or to be
invented, without permission in writing from the publisher, except by a reviewer
who wishes to quote brief passages in connection with a review written for
inclusion in a magazine, newspaper, or broadcast.

Library of Congress Cataloging in Publication Data
    Drotar, David L.
      Microsurgery: revolution in the operating room.

      1. Microsurgery.   2. Microsurgery—History.
    I. Title.
    RD33.6.D76   617'.05   81-3850
    ISBN 0-8253-0056-8   AACR2

Published in the United States by Beaufort Books, Inc., New York.
Published simultaneously in Canada by General Publishing Co. Limited

Printed in the U.S.A.   First Edition
10 9 8 7 6 5 4 3 2 1

For ARNOLD MADISON, *whose friendship and professionalism never wane.*

2195960

Acknowledgments

The author would like to thank the following people for the very valuable resources they provided: Pauline C. Bartel, Dorothy H. Drotar, Arnold Madison, Pat Somerscales, Darlene C. Weaver, and, of course, "The Group."

Contents

Introduction

In Tampa, Florida, Karl woke to the sun streaming through the hospital window onto his bed. The warmth encased his muscular body like the snug wet suit he had worn only last week in his college's diving expedition.

Both his eyes squinted in the bright light. Karl stretched his legs under the sheets. Why was he here? Why wasn't he jogging on the beach on such a beautiful morning? He tried to stretch his arms above his head.

Then he remembered.

His left arm was gone. It was still "in the shop" for repairs. Today, however, was the day the doctor had promised the limb would be reattached. In just a few hours, Karl would be wheeled into the operating room. In just a few weeks, he would be splashing in the surf again.

Science fiction?

Yes, the above account is fictional. But theoretically, this could be a common scene in several years. And the technique that would make it possible is microsurgery—performing operations with miniature instruments under high-powered microscopes. Already the procedure has proved highly successful in restoring accidentally severed body parts to their owners. Fingers, hands, arms, and even entire legs have been sewn back onto the body with forty to ninety percent of function regained.

Suppose our diver, Karl, had complained of a sore left elbow. His doctor would analyze the X-rays and lab tests, and discover a malignant bone tumor. An operation to remove the tumor would carry the risk of spreading it to the rest of the body. So, a microsurgeon would amputate the arm, identifying and keeping each blood vessel intact by securing it with clamps. Then the arm would be shipped off to a laboratory where the tumor could be removed, and dangerous doses of chemicals are far away from Karl's critical bodily functions. Finally, after the tumor-killing substance has been cleansed from the arm, and several days of tests confirm the absence of malignancy, the microsurgeon could reattach the arm.

Reimplantation of body parts is just one example of the many areas in which microsurgery is considered a major medical breakthrough. The techniques, however, can be applied to virtually every form of surgery. Entirely new dimensions have opened up. Prior to the development of microsurgery, conventional methods had proved inadequate in such delicate feats as a tumor removed in the pituitary gland, which is located dangerously close to the brain. "We're doing things today that we wouldn't have even dreamed of attempting five years ago," says Dr. Rollin Daniel of Montreal's Royal Victoria Hospital.

In the world of medicine, innovations continually spring up, gain attention, and occasionally may be reported by the news media. For example, Dr. Linus Pauling's work with vitamin C received widespread coverage. But rarely does an entire new discipline emerge, as is the case before us now. Microsurgery is fast becoming a household word. The focal point of any hospital is its operating room. New discoveries, new advances culminate here. *Microsurgery: Revolution in the Operating Room* will explore these frontiers of medicine.

1
Behind the Miracles

As is frequently the case with many past inventions, the practical application of a device to specific areas of technology often follows years later. But when research and applied science finally mesh, the accomplishments may be remarkable. When lasers were first invented in the 1950s, their uses were limited. Today, they are employed in many facets of our life, from the grocery checkout counter to sophisticated communications networks. In the same way, microsurgery was so new that in 1979 only one hundred people in the United States were trained in its special techniques.

The invention of the microscope is analogous to that of the laser, both once having limited uses and developing practical applications. Certainly when Zacharias Janssen, a spectacle maker from the Netherlands, presented a clumsy, six-foot-long microscope to the archduke of Austria in 1590, Janssen did not foresee the wonders that would be performed centuries later with his device. Alas, a generation passed before any serious scientific observations could be attributed to the microscope.

Then in the seventeenth century, the Dutch youth, Anton van Leeuwenhoek went to the city of Amsterdam as a shop assistant, only to return shortly afterward to his home town of Delft, where he spent the remainder of his life. Here, he sold dry goods and performed janitorial duties in city hall.

In his spare time, however, Leeuwenhoek built microscopes, improving on the design of earlier ones by using short-focus single lenses in place of double lenses and by increasing the magnifying power of the scopes. He is often falsely credited as the microscope's inventor having constructed a total of 247 microscopes during his lifetime. Although he did not have a scientific education, his keen powers of observation compensated for his lack of formal training. He would have several instruments set up at the same time and then would meticulously record all he saw.

Leeuwenhoek's most significant observation, in terms of its relevance to our story, was the sighting of movement—he used the term "little beasties" for the minute swimming particles, which we now know as bacteria—inside a drop of rain water. The brilliant researcher had uncovered a new world that had previously been hidden from human eyes! That world was the sphere of all living things.

Leeuwenhoek wrote about his findings and expanded his studies to hematology—the study of blood. His work in this area is considered a classic. He described the circulation of blood through tissue and distinguished the various types of vessels through which it flows, as well as characterizing the blood cells themselves. The structure of the eye, teeth, skin and muscles were all revealed through Leeuwenhoek's microscopic investigation.

Nevertheless, there were limitations placed on the technology of this period. The simple, uncorrected lenses often distorted the color and shape of the image. However, in the next two centuries vast improvements were made in the mechanical and optical properties of the microscope. During the eighteenth century brass was used in the device's construction; in the nineteenth century, new types of glass eliminated the distortion problem. Later, although refinements to the instrument and specialized microscopic methods were developed, no new significant optical advances were made.

All the while, the microscope was proving an invaluable laboratory tool, both for routine diagnosis and for research. It was not until the twentieth century, however, when it was moved into the operating room, that the medical profession began to think of the microscope's application to actual surgical procedures.

During the 1920s, ear surgeons in Sweden put the ordinary laboratory microscope to work. They found that precise manipulations of the miniature structures inside the human ear were made possible by peering through a microscope.

Ophthalmologists in the 1940s were also aided by the increased range of visibility the microscope provided in their work. The limiting factor in performing transplants of the cornea—the transparent tissue covering the eye—had been the inability to accurately place stitches at the proper depth. Going too deep with the needle could puncture underlying membranes and allow the fluid that fills the eye to leak out. Doing the delicate operation with the help of a microscope reduced this possibility.

Interestingly, these successful attempts at microsurgery did not cause its general use. Another major obstacle still had to be overcome before the technique could be applied on a more widespread basis: the joining of blood vessels.

These tiny tubes often have a diameter no larger than a pin's head. The prime source of difficulty was maintaining a free opening at the junction of the two vessels. After vessel ends are matched perfectly so that the tunnels line up, a dozen or more stitches must be sewn. These sutures must be tight enough to hold the tubes closed without pinching or tearing the walls.

Dr. Julius Jacobson, a vascular surgeon at the Mary Fletcher Hospital of the University of Vermont's medical school, led the pioneering efforts in this area. In 1957, he began experimenting with animal blood vessels, searching for the ideal combination of suture material, surgical clamps, and needles. The instruments on hand were too bulky for such extremely detailed work so the resourceful doctor turned to a local jewelry store where he obtained miniature implements originally designed for repairing watches.

Dr. Jacobson recalls those early days. "We even devised a quick test to find out if we could use the instrument. If a jeweler's forceps could pick off a single hair from the back of the hand without slipping or cutting it, we figured it had the ability to grasp a tiny blood vessel."

Once one problem was solved, another quickly took its place. For example, after a suitable clamp was found to grip the vessel, another improvised set of tools had to be positioned to hold the clamp solidly enough for the surgeon to work on the vessel. This often resulted in a collection of hardware resembling Rube-Goldberg devices. Dr. Jacobson continued to whittle away at the technical difficulties and was soon stitching blood vessels as small as one millimeter in diameter. He even influenced reluctant American manufacturers to produce instruments more suitable to microsurgery.

On May 23, 1962, a headline-making case took place at

Massachusetts General Hospital in Boston. Dr. Ronald A. Malt performed the world's first successful limb reattachment on twelve-year-old Little League pitcher, Everett Knowles. The boy had tried to jump on a freight train and had his right arm ripped off below the shoulder. The detached flesh still dangling inside his sleeve, Everett naively assumed that his arm would simply be sewn back on.

"Somehow the idea didn't seem so farfetched," says Dr. Malt, who reports today his patient can lift eighty pounds with that arm.

Although this case prompted other surgeons to try reattaching body parts that had been severed in home or industrial accidents, work in this area progressed slowly in the United States. Meanwhile, the Chinese blend of modern and ancient medicine produced a unique success story. Far removed from the technology available to developed nations, Chinese surgeons reattached body parts at an astounding rate. The supply of patients was largely due to a constant stream of accident victims from industry.

One chilly December, a worker's arm was sliced off in a diesel-engine accident. The cold weather worked to the man's advantage, because it preserved the arm while he made the long trek through the countryside to the Sixth People's Hospital in Shanghai. Here, the arm was reattached under a microscope after a total of thirty-six hours since its detachment.

Chief surgeon Yu Zhongjia reports that 287 limb reattachment operations were performed at the center between 1963 and 1978. Of these, eighty-six percent were successful. The success rate for the more difficult task of reattaching fingers climbed from about fifty percent to greater than ninety percent when the surgical microscope, specifically designed for the operating room, became available to China in 1973.

The fact that a patient and his reclaimed body part survive the surgery is not the only criterion for success. Other factors, such as range of joint motion, sensation, and muscular strength are also considered by doctors. On this basis, approximately sixty percent of the hospital's cases were said to be functionally successful, and about half of these were able to go back to their original jobs.

The Chinese did not limit their work to the reattachment of arms, legs, feet, and fingers. They soon entered unprecedented territory when they succeeded in reconstructing a human hand from other parts of the body. In 1974, both hands of Kao Tiansue were blown away by an explosive. Surgeons at the Sixth People's Hospital removed two of the patient's toes—a big toe and a little toe—and attached them opposite each other to a prosthetic palm, which was implanted in the wrist. The advantage of such a claw-like hand over an entirely mechanical one is that it is flexible as well as being sensitive to touch. In fact, Kao is now able to manipulate the hand well enough to paint the delicate characters of Chinese calligraphy. In general, Chinese medical progress is not well documented in professional literature, but most U.S. doctors credit the Chinese as being the first in the world to create a new hand.

The Chinese certainly earned their international reputation for work in the field of microsurgery. In 1979, they were ahead of all other nations in the number of limb attachments performed. But a revived interest by professionals in the United States during recent years has been the biggest boost to the "industry."

David Glenn Jackson was standing in a Tennessee zinc mine on March 31, 1977, when a cable snapped and a piece of metal siding dropped down the shaft. As he tried to push a co-worker to safety, the metal struck and sliced off both his own arms. Rushed to a nearby hospital, he received emergency treatment; his arms were packed in plastic and ice. Then he was transferred to Jewish Hospital in Louisville, Kentucky, where special microsurgery teams reimplanted the arms.

Several operations were required over a period of time in order to graft skin and tendons into the arms. Three years later one of the surgeons, Dr. Joseph E. Kutz, cautioned that Jackson was still in the recovery stage. "He's doing very well, but it takes a while for this type of thing to get up to standards." The Louisville center is now handling an average of one thousand microsurgery cases per year. The science is rapidly expanding into other hospitals and medical centers across the country. Dr. Bruce Shafiroff, another member of the surgical team at Jewish Hospital, has recently moved to Syracuse, New York, where he directs the development of the newly-formed microsurgery unit at Upstate Medical Center. Dr. Shafiroff feels that the sudden proliferation of microsurgery is tilting it out of proportion. He admits it is different and special but does not think it deserves a status apart from all other surgery. Claiming that new developments and case histories should be carried in existing medical journals, he scoffs at the premise of the specialized microsurgery journals now being published.

"There's no such thing as a microsurgeon," Dr. Shafiroff says. "Microsurgery is merely a technique to help you do an operation better."

Nevertheless public attention *has* been focused on the topic. Almost every week a major newspaper carries an article about some wonder of microsurgery, and local television stations run features on its doctors and patients. Whichever way the doctor wishes to be acknowledged, he or she is undeniably a special breed spawned by contemporary society.

2
The Microsurgeon

Who is the microsurgeon? If this science is a specialized type of surgery, what attributes set its practitioners apart from other surgeons?

The primary qualification for a microsurgeon never appears on his job resume—patience. The long hours involved in conventional surgery are often considered grueling, but microsurgery places additional demands on the doctor's stamina. It is not uncommon for replant and other delicate surgical procedures to last twelve to eighteen hours. Dr. Berish Strauch, of Montefiore Hospital in the Bronx, New York, worked on and off for twenty-two hours reconnecting the severed hand of a Bronx boy, Ricky Barnett, which was cut off by a mixer in the bagel shop where he worked. Dr. Andrew C. Novich, a microsurgeon specializing in urology at Cleveland Clinic in Ohio, states, "You must proceed slowly. There is no way to rush. It's a

21

very laborious type of work that takes enormous concentration. In fact, most surgeons can't stay at it for more than five hours at a time."

The physical demands this type of prolonged intense concentration places on the body are rigorous and, indeed, shape the physician's lifestyle. He must maintain a high level of fitness. Some jog, swim, or play squash to keep in shape. Most do not smoke. Coffee and tea are generally avoided at least twenty-four hours before surgery, because caffeine might cause slight trembling in the hands and fingers. Even strenuous lifting could cause a disastrous muscle quiver long afterward, so the surgeon does not do any heavy chores before going into the operating room. And, of course, a good night's sleep gives the surgeon a fresh start on the day.

One dominant characteristic crucial to the microsurgeon's psychological makeup is an overriding concern for the patient. The patient must feel secure and place a high degree of trust in the doctor. The surgeon must believe that the patient comes first.

Microsurgeons should be able to transcend their egos and be inwardly directed by a sense of purpose. Indeed, this attitude is necessary to avoid succumbing to the "miracle-worker" syndrome, a condition fostered by the laudatory labels the media attaches to the work. This in turn leads to a feeling of mutual respect between doctor and patient, a relationship that is essential for successful treatment and healing.

At the present time, the profession consists primarily of male microsurgeons. Although the sex ratio mirrors that of the other surgical specialties, this is not to say that it is a closed field. Microsurgery is an expanding science with many new openings in a whole range of specialized areas. One woman who has seized such opportunity and gained prominence is Dr. Julia Terzis, affiliated with Royal Victoria Hospital. Located in Montreal and considered a leading microsurgical center in North America, the hospital was the site of Dr. Terzis's pioneering work in the microsurgery of nerves.

Her skills were instrumental in the case of Beth McFadden, an eleven-year-old girl whose right leg was cut off by a commuter train on Long Island, New York. Operations to replant the leg and connect blood vessels were done before the girl was transferred to Montreal. Dr. Terzis then went to work on the scrambled nerves. Not only is her work useful in the manipulation of tissue, but she is contributing to the body of scientific knowledge of how nerves actually function. Other impressive work involves developing techniques for restoring sensation to paralysis victims by transplanting nerves from other parts of the body to the affected area.

The microsurgeon does not work in isolation and is an integral part of a team composed of other surgeons, anesthesiologists, operating-room nurses, and technicians. Many hospitals have actually assembled special microsurgery crews who are on standby for emergency procedures such as limb reattachments. In instances such as these, teamwork is especially important. Individual characteristics must fuse in a unique blend of competence, accuracy, and precision timing.

In the July 31, 1978 issue of *People* magazine, a personality profile of microsurgeon Dr. Harold Kleinert of Louisville's Jewish Hospital portrays him as a relaxed, stable person interacting with his staff in a setting of genuine comradeship. He is quoted by the interviewer: "Long ago, I realized that if you got into a critical situation in the operating room, you would need a team that was ready to work, not one you'd gotten emotionally upset."

Dr. Kleinert's admiring staff does not remember his ever getting angry and yelling, but they do recall the time he told dirty jokes while operating on a patient who was still conscious. The patient later complained, "You bet it bothered me. Kleinert talks so low I couldn't hear any of the punch lines."

A high level of pride is just as applicable to the microsurgeon's workmanship as it is to any artisan's product. The surgeon is a talented craftsman who takes pleasure in seeing a procedure completed in the most aesthetic way. A sloppy job would never do.

Obvoiusly the capacity to perform the detailed microscopic maneuvers requires meticulous training. "There's nothing about a microscope that makes the blood vessel any larger, the tumor less adherent, or the nerve less fragile," explains Dr. R. M. Peardon Donaghy of the University of Vermont Medical School's neurosurgery division. The surgeon must have total mastery and control over the instruments, guiding them through fraction-of-an-inch motions. Frequently the entire area in which a major operation takes place is no larger than a fingernail.

Perhaps learning how to work in this new dimension involves more retraining than training. Anybody who has gone through medical school has stared at countless slides under a microscope. A true perception of size, however, is never fully gained until one tries to perform an action that will alter the image. When you think you're moving a molecule, you may well end up launching the specimen. The lens not only magnifies the structures; it grossly exaggerates their motion. Would-be microsurgeons usually find they can't even hold an implement steady enough under the microscope. The rock-steadiness and exact hand-eye coordination come only through practice during a long apprenticeship.

A skilled doctor with years of traditional operating experience still requires many hours of practice in the laboratory before attaining proficiency at microsurgical methods. The first technique to learn is the joining of two vessels. Small sections of plastic tubing are pieced back together by making miniature stitches with tiny needles. Because the eye is not yet accustomed to the spatial differences, the initial tendency is to move the instrument above or below the intended point of contact. While making a suture during nonmicroscopic surgery, the surgeon might move the tip of the needle through a five-inch arc. However, in the miniaturized version of the same motion, the tip would travel through an arc only an eighth of an inch.

The new trainee might begin by sewing one-millimeter tubes. Then as skill is acquired, smaller and smaller tubes are attempted. Real blood vessels are tackled next; there is a ready supply from laboratory animals. If cadavers are available, their blood vessels are ideal, of course, matching those of a living person. The surgeon uses sutures that measure only eighteen microns in diameter (a micron is one-thousandth of a millimeter), so small they could pass through a human hair or a single red blood cell. One can see that tying knots in the wispy filament of the tubes becomes an even more complex task.

Once the student feels confident in his or her ability to produce a snug, leakproof seal, he graduates to replanting animal ears and digits. During the 1960s, Dr. Harry Buncke of San Mateo, California, a pioneer in the development of microsurgical tools, often took this same route when he was testing his homemade devices. Sewing an ear back onto a rabbit or a finger onto a monkey most closely approximated human conditions; the blood vessels in these parts of the animals are roughly the same size as the smallest of man.

Although surgeons must acquire the manual skills in a step-by-step fashion, other pieces in their overall training may occur simultaneously with, or prior to, the lab experience. A small audience clustered around a closed-circuit television screen is a common scene near an operating room where a microsurgery operation is taking place. The unfolding drama of the surgery and the detailed techniques used are being watched closely by all, while also being recorded on videotape for further study in the future.

Where does a surgeon go for formal training in microsurgery? A medical center such as Hand Surgery Associates of Louisville, Kentucky, offers a good base for surgeons coming from a wide range of specialties. Three months to a year may be spent at becoming adept with microinstruments, but some extremely complicated procedures take considerably longer to master. The techniques to reverse female sterilization, for example, require about one hundred laboratory hours to learn and an additional year of practice before true facility is accomplished. Special intensive workshops in areas of particular interest may be given to surgeons as needs arise. In May, 1979, neurosurgeons at Johns Hopkins began offering one-week microsurgery courses that drew doctors from all over the United States. Some prefer a less structured environment, and many surgeons make private arrangements to learn skills from an experienced colleague.

After the initial investment of training time, an accomplished microsurgeon does not soon forget his craft. Like learning how to ride a bicycle, the skill is not lost during periods of inactivity. However, most surgeons *do* prefer to keep their skills tuned and practice regularly, much like musicians between concerts. Upstate Medical Center in Syracuse has a special laboratory where microsurgeons can replay their techniques. It's also a good place for a doctor to relearn a method that had not been fully developed when he or she first started using it. Perhaps the surgeon had taught the skill to himself or herself and now wants to learn the current technique with all its innovations.

Supported by an arsenal of professional traits and highly sophisticated skills, the microsurgeon is ready to enter the operating room.

3
Techniques and Tools of the Trade

As we have seen, the development that has made micro-surgery feasible is the expansion of the surgeon's visual horizon so that small structures can be dealt with success-fully. Human fingers are able to make infinitesimal motions as long as the eye can perceive them and send this informa-tion back to the brain. Controlled single movements of as little as one micron, one thousandth of a millimeter, have been measured by special gauges.

In addition to magnification, a very important quality of the optical device "is resolution," the ability of the device to separately distinguish the lines of the image. If a structure is merely enlarged but the details blend or merge together, the surgeon has not gained any advantage.

During the initial preparation of the tissue area, the

microsurgeon may wear eyeglasses that have protruding telescopic-like lenses attached. Resembling jeweler's eyepieces, the lenses are called optical loupes and provide magnification in the range of two-and-a-half to six times actual size of the structure. The glasses are worn on the head in conjunction with a headlight, which supplies illumination to the area. Loupes are most useful while clearing away debris and dissecting—separating the operating site from surrounding tissue—prior to the actual stitching of blood vessels, nerves, or whatever. Loupes are not practical, however, when doing more detailed work. Since the lenses are only as stationary as the surgeon's head, the movements at higher levels of magnification become distracting. At this point it becomes necessary to rely on a fixed source of optics.

Basic to the science of microsurgery is, of course, the microscope. We have seen how it has played an integral part in surgical developments. Many companies now manufacture numerous sophisticated models designed specifically with the surgeon in mind. Magnifications from two-and-a-half to about fifty times are the most useful during operating procedures, and, therefore, this is the most common range on these scopes. Foot pedals that permit the viewer to change magnification and to focus an image are frequently incorporated into the engineering. This setup eases cumbersome adjustments and allows the surgeon to keep hands and eyes fixed on the site of the operation. Similarly, foot-controlled zoom lenses can zero in on a structure precisely when needed, averting a potentially critical interruption of the procedure.

Three-dimensional vision is absolutely mandatory if the surgeon is to gain any "feel" for the already-distorted perspective. Peering through a single eyepiece produces a flat image. Two eyepieces arranged side by side in binocular fashion, however, produce what is known as stereoscopic vision, which is the way we actually see the world. Each eye (or eyepiece) produces its own slightly different image, and the brain combines these into one. When stereoscopic vision is employed in microscopy, the image reveals the original texture and contours of the specimen, resulting in enhanced resolution.

Operating microscopes today are usually not limited to serving one surgeon at a time. Often another set of binocular eyepieces are mounted opposite the first, enabling a second member of the surgical team to simultaneously participate, or allowing a medical student to observe the action. In addition, the two fields are independent of each other with separate controls for each. This feature allows each viewer to look at only his own field or to permit both to focus on the same spot. Microsurgical scopes are now available having three or more viewing heads and costing almost one hundred thousand dollars.

Without proper lighting, a microscope is practically useless. In modern microscopes, the lighting system that enables the surgeon to see the specimen area is internal to the machine. That is, light is projected through the lenses onto the tissue where the operation is taking place. This arrangement prevents the microsurgeon's hands and tools from casting shadows which could block the view.

Photographic attachments to the microscope are available that permit the doctor to take 35-millimeter color slides of particularly interesting or critical steps. One such system, developed by Dr. John P. Beale, Jr. of the San Francisco Eye and Ear Hospital uses a miniature color television camera to scan the operation and project the site onto a monitor. The surgeon can look at the monitor, at the microscope, or directly at the tissue. This alleviates some of the strain associated with holding the head in a fixed position for an extended period of time. Additionally, a blown-up image on a wall-mounted television screen allows other doctors to see the work. Videotaping the operation serves for review or instructional use afterward. Various multi-functional microscopic systems leave the hospital or medical center contemplating a purchase with a dazzling array of accessories from which to choose depending upon the particular surgical application.

Paralleling the advances in optics and the great strides in techniques, was the development of more advanced tools. Ordinary surgical instruments appeared heavy and awkward under magnification. "Incredibly, as American expertise in reconstructing needle-thin blood vessels matured, surgeons still had to rely on razor blades and other do-it-yourself paraphernalia, because manufacturers refused to believe a market existed for microsurgical tools," reported a 1975 article in *Science Digest*.

The thread required for microsurgical stitching is as thin as the strands of a spider's web—as little as one-tenth the width of a human hair and practically invisible—yet it must be able to withstand repeated tension. Sometimes as many as thirty sutures are used when connecting two vessels. In his early days of microsurgery, Dr. Harry Buncke used the filament from a silkworm's cocoon. Today, ultra-thin fibers are produced from nylon and other polymers.

The procurement of a tiny needle was also subject to the ingenuity of pioneering microsurgeons. Here, Dr. Buncke teamed up with Werner Schultz, a German microelectronics professional, to produce a needle from nylon. This was done by electroplating a chromium tip onto the end of a nylon thread. Since that time, commercial suppliers have come to produce all-metal needles with the necessary "eyes."

Specialized microinstruments now come in all shapes. So

tiny are the suturing needles, for example, that they are too small to be held by the human hand. Instead, they are placed in holders which are in turn manipulated by the operator. The tips of scissors can barely be seen by the unaided eye. Forceps are extremely fragile; accidentally dropping them only one-half inch could cause damage which renders them useless. Probes, hooks, clamps, scalpels, and irrigation ducts all made from titanium, a very lightweight metal, are scaled down into lilliputian size. As a professional tennis player uses the racket that best fits his hand and style, the surgeon should do the same and consider his own individuality when selecting instruments. Just as power tools make the carpenter's job easier, so such miniature counterparts are of benefit to the microsurgeon's tasks. A tiny electric drill with a liquid-cooled bit chomps through bone, maintaining a clear surgical site and reducing the possibility of heat damage. Other tools have elaborate pneumatic and hydraulic controls that permit continuous, smooth operation.

One very important advance that holds great promise for certain microsurgical procedures is the laser, which has been used with great success in gynecological operations. Lasers are, basically, highly focused beams of light energy. What do they accomplish that ordinary tools can't? In a nonmicrosurgical operation a small amount of fluid usually collects in the wound area. This is not a problem. However, a single drop of blood under a microscopic procedure can totally obliterate the surgeon's field of view. A method to keep the surgical area dry would greatly improve efficiency —and the laser provides the means. Blood and lymphatic vessels can be pinpointed and sealed by the laser's concentrated light beam without damaging the surrounding tissue.

The variety of equipment now being produced is impressive. These tools of the trade are not cheap, however, and the cost prohibits some doctors from entering the field of microsurgery. Each surgeon needs his own individually fitted tools and could easily have eight thousand dollars invested in instruments alone. This figure does not include microscopes and laser units, which are owned by the hospital.

We are living in the Computer Age and its impact is strongly felt in the domain of medicine. At the Royal Victoria Hospital in Montreal, doctors use nerve diagrams produced by computers. They can take the sterile paper into the operating room and follow its pattern when reconnecting severed nerves, much like a repair-person will follow an electronic diagram when fixing a television set.

First reported in 1980 by scientific journals was a computerized system invented by Doctors K. Buol Heslin and Richard K. Mackool, which has reduced much of the risk of certain kinds of eye surgery. One of the unit's functions is to maintain constant eye pressure during the operation. If fluid leaves the eye, the machine monitors it and replaces the exact amount. Before this system was available, there existed the dangerous possibility of liquid leaving the eye at a faster rate than it was being replaced. But now a state of equilibrium can be maintained while the microsurgeon is working.

As strange as it may sound in this era of computerized electronic assistance, the ancient remedy of applying leeches is being used in microsurgery. During medieval times, the worms were gathered and used extensively in Europe as a panacea for every imaginable ailment. The inch-long creatures contain a chemical called hirudin which prevents clotting as they suck blood from their human hosts where they are applied. The "leeching" practice died out as statistics revealed that losing blood was not a good way to treat disease.

Today at the Hôpital Saint André in Bordeaux, France, Professor Jacques Baudet and Dr. Jean-Louis Bovet have successfully used the parasites to draw blood from plastic surgery patients when blood clots threaten the outcome of an operation.

In finger reimplantation cases, this leech method has indispensable applications. Severed arteries are reconnected under the microscope, but often surgeons are unsuccessful in mending the smaller veins in the fingertips. In this case the blood might flow under the fingernail and create pressure which causes clots in the arteries. Thus the normal circulation of blood is halted, and the cells do not receive adequate nourishment and oxygen. The purpose of using leeches is to prevent blood clotting long enough so that new blood vessels will grow into the implanted tip and drain the stagnant blood. The Bordeaux doctors had previously made a cut on the end of the finger in these cases, but excessive bleeding was a problem and sometimes transfusions were necessary.

Even squeamish patients generally adjust quickly to the leech treatment; they realize the finger is at stake if they don't comply. The microsurgeons prescribe one critter in the morning and one at night—up to ten a day for extreme cases. The cycle is repeated each day for as many as nine days.

Doctors Baudet and Bovet have visited several surgical centers in the United States and believe it or not, their unorthodox technique is gaining popularity. At the Montefiore Hospital in the Bronx, New York, several fingers have been saved as a result of leech therapy coupled with microsurgery. Dr. Jane A. Petro is stocking up on the parasites because a ready supply is not always available in emergency situations. She has recently imported one hundred leeches from France.

Inside the operating room, several procedures are becoming standard in most microsurgical operations. The microscope is usually cloaked with a sterile cover to guard against infection. In fact, when extreme precautions must be taken, the patient may be entirely surrounded with an isolation drape that has individual pockets for each of the microimplements needed during the operation. More and more of the automated tools are being designed with removable units that can be placed inside an autoclave chamber, a device for sterilizing equipment under high pressure.

The patient must be completely immobilized because even small twitches appear as upheavals under the microscope. The doctor's hands and arms rest next to each other on a flat object to avoid any wrist or arm trembling, and the microscope is adjusted so that the surgeon sits straight-backed and does not have to lean forward. A special microsurgery chair has been developed that braces the entire body in the correct position and alleviates some of the strain during the long ordeal.

Such extreme preparations are necessary considering the length of the average operation. The smaller the reattached part, the longer the process takes. Each severed finger requires two to six hours of work. When a case involves several amputation sites, the work is compounded, and the surgeons take turns. One shift might work at putting an arm back in place. The next might reattach a thumb, and the last crew might handle two fingers. The patient could easily end up spending an entire day in surgery.

The final ingredient necessary for a successful microsurgery procedure does not lie in the operating room. A competent intensive care unit provides the grand finale after the surgery.

4
You Gotta Have Heart

So far, when we have discussed the techniques of micro-surgery, we have most often referred to the joining of blood vessels. Although we will see in later chapters that the techniques apply to other structures in the body as well, most microsurgery *does* involve the circulatory system.

During life's early beginnings, single-celled organisms floated in a sea that provided for all their needs. Nourish-ment was simply absorbed through a thin membrane and wastes drifted away. The complexity of larger life forms, however, demanded a more active method of providing food for the many cells. So, fluid was pumped throughout the body by a special kind of organ called a heart.

Cardiovascular system is the term applied when speak-ing of the heart and blood vessels as a unit; the human heart is the strongest muscle in the human body. In the span of one minute, the entire blood supply passes through the heart, having been pumped once around the body through tubes called blood vessels. If laid end to end, the body's blood vessels would stretch for sixty thousand miles. The system is so extensive that each cell is always within a hair's width of the blood supply.

The blood vessels are specialized, according to their functions. Arteries are responsible for the flow of blood away from the heart; veins return the blood. The connections between the two are called capillaries, and it is here that the exchange of nutrients and wastes takes place. Food is processed by the digestive system, and the chemically broken-down material is absorbed into the bloodstream. Oxygen enters the bloodstream in the lungs. Both these substances are released at the appropriate body cell when needed. Carbon dioxide and other waste products from cellular activities are picked up by the blood. Capillary walls are so thin that blood cells pass single file within them, and the fluids of the blood and tissues can freely exchange substances directly through the walls.

What happens to the waste products once they enter the bloodstream? Obviously an efficient mechanism must be present to continually replenish the blood or otherwise the whole system would work for only one trip around the body. The lungs and the kidneys assist with the maintenance duties. Blood circulates through the lungs where the carbon dioxide is dispersed through exhaling, and a fresh supply of oxygen is supplied by inhaling. The kidneys filter out liquid wastes that are eventually expelled from the body as urine.

As we grow older, components of the cardiovascular system can malfunction, and microsurgery is being used to repair diseased vessels. Arteries are particularly vulnerable to the effects of age. As fat is deposited on their walls, the vessels become more brittle and narrow. This places an added strain on the heart, which must pump harder to force

37

blood through the constricted arteries, which in turn can reduce the amount of blood that ultimately reaches the cells. If this happens in the brain, it can become critically dangerous, because brain cells cannot be deprived of oxygen, even for a short period of time. Here microsurgery enters the scene. When vessels have reached this clogged stage, surgery purges fatty plaques from the miniscule brain arteries.

Just as cells such as those found in the brain and in the muscles are fed by the blood, so, too, is every area in the body nourished by blood flow making virtually all organs candidates for vascular microsurgery. Consider the case of a forty-four-year-old woman in Ohio who enters a hospital with only her right kidney intact—the left one had become diseased several years ago and was removed. Now one of the arteries in the good kidney is found to contain an aneurysm, an abnormal blood-filled swelling resulting from a weakened vessel wall. The problem with conventional surgery is the inaccessibility of the puffy, balloon-type formation. The woman faces the grim prospect of having to live the rest of her life taking treatments on a dialysis machine to cleanse her blood.

But microsurgery presents a better alternative. The doctor removes the kidney from the patient, who is not on dialysis during the operation, severing all connections to her body. Then he is able to remove the aneurysm and repair the artery. Next the renovated organ is put back, and the microscope assists in the long process of joining seven delicate arteries, whose reconnections take almost one hour each. Sutures must be strong enough to prevent the blood from leaking but not so tight that they stop normal flow. The operation is a success and the woman returns home in ten days.

* * *

One of microsurgery's most exciting and notable applications is the new-found ability to transfer large chunks of tissue from one part of the body to another. Major sections of bone, muscle, or skin can be taken from a healthy body area to compensate for damaged tissue. The skin in the donor area is then stretched and sewn together if at all possible; if not, skin grafts are used to cover this area.

On a rainy night in May, 1979, David Horning of Lafayette, New York, was on his way home from Syracuse University. He rode his motorcycle over a hill and suddenly collided with a car parked on the wrong side of the road. The impact wedged his right leg between the motorcycle and the car's bumper, ripping out skin, bone, and muscle below the knee.

Medical attention over the next several months consisted of a temporary metal brace and stopgap measures to curb infection. The body's normal immune responses at the site had been destroyed because vessel routes were severed and germ fighting agents could not reach the area. Once this problem was under control with drugs, actual repair of the leg could be attempted by the procedure known as a free-tissue transfer.

In the nineteen-and-one-half hour operation, Dr. Bruce Shafiroff and Dr. John Mosher paired their microsurgical talents to refill the cyclist's literally "hollow"—an empty shell after skin, bone and muscle was ripped out—leg with other parts from his own body. A piece of fibula, the smaller of the leg's two lower bones, was substituted for the crushed tibia, the shinbone. In its new position, this replacement grew to the diameter of the original bone it replaced. Skin from Horning's back was then sewn over the exposed wound. All the while, the blood vessels of the new parts were exactly matched and joined with their companion arteries and veins in the surrounding tissue so that a continuous flow of blood was established up and down the leg.

During the delicate operation, David Horning lost a great deal of blood; the possibility of amputation still loomed. The two doctors encouraged their patient not to give up hope, and the leg was saved. About those early feelings, Horning says, "I never really thought I was ever going to lose the leg—well, almost never. But amputation was unacceptable. I knew I would walk again. I was determined. And Dr. Shafiroff and Dr. Mosher were with me all the way."

The technique of free-tissue transfer was first used in 1972 and has since been used many times on people who have lost large areas of skin. In these instances, the operation is more frequently referred to as a "free-flap" transfer.

Prior to this innovation, the course of treatment was done in several agonizing steps that were spread over months or years. For example, a flap of skin might be cut from an uninjured arm, leaving one edge attached like the fold on a hinged box top of opened detergent. This piece of living skin was then sewn onto the missing section. The patient often had to assume very uncomfortable and tiring positions—an arm attached to a face, or two legs fused together. After new blood vessels formed and the transfer of skin to the recipient locale was completed, the connected parts were severed. The procedure was feasible only if appropriate donor parts were undamaged. Extensive mutilation, such as the Horning case, would rule out any hope for even this treatment.

Of course, free-flap and free-tissue transfers are not the miracle cure-all for every patient. Some accidents are so destructive that enough good tissue doesn't remain to be borrowed. And there are still some problems that are not yet resolved: More refined knowledge about donor sites needs to be gathered; the relationship between blood clotting and damaged blood vessels is still not fully understood. Despite these drawbacks, this area of microsurgery holds great potential.

Free flaps have already given new meaning to plastic surgery; cancer victims who have had a tumor removed particularly benefit from this procedure. Previous policy with these patients was to leave the wound open for a year so that cancer recurrence could be monitored. Particularly with facial cancers, this approach was highly disruptive to the person's psychological health, and suicide often resulted. Now, microsurgeons can repair almost any skin defect using free flaps and establishing circulation to the area.

If any particular operation could be called a classic in the short time span that microsurgery has developed, that operation would be the now famous carotid bypass, a procedure to divert more blood into the brain and ward off potential strokes. In the United States, a half-million people undergo strokes each year and, of these, more than 200,000 die. A stroke results when blood is suddenly shut off to the brain. This organ's extremely complex activities require a high level of energy which must be maintained continuously—there are no energy reserves like those found in the muscles. If the brain is deprived of blood for more than four minutes, permanent damage occurs. Such damage within the brain can cause paralysis and death, not to mention complete loss of all thought and motor processes.

Strokes generally begin when a blockage of the arteries, which supply blood to the brain, occurs. The culprit in most cases, a clot becomes lodged by the thickened artery wall. Long before a fatal attack occurs, however, most potential victims will have a warning signal in the form of a minor stroke. Slurred speech, partial blindness or numbness on one side of the body results.

Stroke victims are prime candidates for a carotid bypass operation. First performed in the Cantonal Hospital in Zurich, Switzerland, by Dr. M. Gazi Zazargil, the operation began in the United States in 1967 at the Medical College of Vermont. Analogous to the coronary bypass operation for patients with heart diseases, the arterial bypass technique attempts to reroute the blood supply around the troublesome carotid area to restore more ample circulation to the brain. Such a feat would not be possible with traditional surgical techniques.

The carotid artery, which supplies the head with blood, runs up the neck and divides into the internal carotid artery and the external carotid artery. The internal carotid feeds the brain, while the external lies on the outer surface of the skull and serves the scalp.

During the carotid bypass, the patient is under general anesthesia; his head is placed in a device that holds it fixed to the operating table. A branch of the external carotid artery is recruited to serve as a donor vessel. Running from the temple across the forehead, the artery is slit just above the eyebrow. One end is stitched closed and left in place. Because the scalp receives enough blood from other arteries there is no danger in eliminating the blood flow from this source.

Next, the surgeon drills a hole about an inch-and-a-half in diameter into the skull above the ear. At this location an extension of the internal carotid lies just below the surface. The surgeon cuts an oval opening into the side of the artery, routes the free end of the forehead vessel to the site and then sews the two together. The blood flow into the interior of the head is now augmented by this additional source of blood from the external carotid artery.

The carotid bypass operation has been shown to be highly successful in stroke prevention. Dr. Duke S. Sampson of the University of Texas Health Sciences Center has published the results of a patient survey which reveals that the procedure is more effective than drugs in warding off strokes. Patients who have already suffered major strokes also benefit from the microsurgery. If the operation to increase the blood supply is done very soon after the attack, brain damage is averted.

We often hear about side effects in medicine and think of them in a negative sense. But the carotid artery bypass has produced some surprising benefits in addition to stroke prevention. Two visual disorders that are caused by insufficient blood flow through the carotid artery are lessened after the bypass operation. Patients who experienced a loss of vision resulting from lack of blood at the retina, the rear portion of the eye, no longer had this problem after the bypass. The severity of a condition in which the patient has excruciating pain in the eye socket is also reduced.

We have seen how the cardiovascular system maintains life support for the entire body, and how microsurgery's role is ever-expanding in this basic area. This is also the case with the microsurgical technique of reattaching body parts —a specialized application which benefits greatly from these vascular techniques.

5
Restoring Body Parts

In 1969, Neil Armstrong made history by becoming the first man to set foot on the moon. His famous words, "That's one small step for man, one giant leap for mankind," again had significance almost a decade later, in 1978, when the astronaut jumped, not from a lunar module, but from a truck. One of Armstrong's ring fingers was torn off during the vault. An operation to replant the digit was successful, attesting to mankind's quantum leap in another area of its technology.

The success rate for reattaching fingers has been climbing. Government statistics show that 1,300 hand and finger reattachment operations occurred in the United States in 1977. Arms, hands, fingers, thumbs, legs, feet, and toes that were severed have been successfully reattached due to the advances in microsurgery. Ninety percent of the operations performed by Dr. Laurence LeWinn of New York Hospital restore normal function to the finger.

The body's appendages form an interface with the environment that can not be underestimated. The legs and feet propel an average person one hundred thousand kilometers during a lifetime. This is more than twice the distance around the earth. The arms and hands are physical extensions of the mind—touching, exploring, taking, rejecting, and creating.

A limb is much more than the sum of its parts, because a limb combines the parts in a complex function. Therefore, the reattachment of a severed element must accomplish more than simply putting the pieces together. A complex structure of blood vessels, bones, tendons, nerves, muscles, and their interactions must be fully understood before any attempt to operate on them can be made.

There are 206 bones in the human body. Together they comprise the skeleton, which forms a framework for the body and gives it shape. Certain bones, such as the skull, spine, and ribs, serve primarily as support and protection, and do not move. Other bones assist the body in producing an infinite variety of motion. Bones are just as alive as other parts of the body. They contain cells and blood vessels and perform all the functions that other live tissue performs, except that their rate of activity is much slower. The amazing ability of bones to withstand pressure—up to twenty-four thousand pounds per square inch—is due to their hollow, cylindrical shape and their coating of crystallized layers of mineral deposits. Forty-five percent of a bone is composed of minerals in the form of calcium phosphate.

Bones are held together by strong connective tissues known as ligaments. The point of meeting—the joint—has a shape that depends on the type of motion that is required. The simple hinge joints in the fingers permit up-and-down motion, for example, while the ball and socket joints of the hips permit movement in several directions. The placement of the thumb bones are particularly unique because these bones are set at a specific angle from the other finger bones, allowing a grasping action.

Of course, bones do not move by themselves; they act as levers which are pulled by muscles. There are over six hundred muscles in the human body, and those that are capable of acting on demand are called voluntary or skeletal muscles. Tough, flexible bands of tissue called tendons bind the muscles to the bones. For movement to occur, one section of a bone pair remains relatively stationary while the other is moved. Skeletal muscles have an elongated shape and the point at which the tapered end is attached to the movable bone is called the insertion.

A skeletal muscle can cause motion only by contracting and thereby pulling the body part in its direction, often with tremendous force. Lifting an arm, for example, causes the large biceps of the upper arm to contract and to draw the bones of the forearm closer. Meanwhile, the opposing triceps muscle on the arm's rear side relaxes. The process is reversed when the arm is lowered. The triceps contracts to pull the arm back and the biceps relaxes.

This team setup occurs with every group of muscles so that movement can always be reversed. The arrangement has the advantage of coordinating forces; while one muscle is moving, the other serves as a brake. Some parts of the body are mobilized by muscles that are relatively remote from their site; for example, muscles in the palm and wrist power the slim, agile fingers.

All this motion is not "free," however. Energy is required to run the system. Ingested foods, primarily sugars and starches, are converted into a single compound, glycogen, which is stored in the muscle cells. When the muscles are called upon to respond, the glycogen is available for quick conversion into energy. This chemical reaction requires oxygen which, as we have seen, is carried in the blood. Therefore, muscle tissue is characterized by a rich supply of blood vessels.

What triggers the muscles to act? Voluntary muscles are controlled by commands from the brain. "Contract" or "relax" signals, which travel via nerves routed through the spinal cord to the individual muscles. Any single body movement is actually a combination of thousands of muscle and nerve interactions. Muscular coordination is developed as the person practices a desired movement over and over again until it requires less conscious thought.

Seventeen-year-old music student Renee Katz had practiced her flute endlessly when her promising career suddenly seemed doomed in the spring of 1979. Waiting for a subway in New York City one evening, she was pushed from the platform by a stranger in the crowd. Renee fell onto the tracks as a train whizzed by and completely severed her right hand.

In the premicrosurgery era, a victim like this couldn't possibly hope to ever use the hand again. Surgeons would merely tidy the amputation site or reattach a nonfunctional, nonfeeling stub. But this case was different. As paramedics were administering emergency first aid to Katz, a policeman placed the severed limb in a plastic bag. Another officer obtained ice from a nearby restaurant to chill the tissue. Girl and hand were rushed to New York University Medical Center where a six-doctor team headed by Drs. Daniel C. Baker and William W. Shaw spent the next sixteen hours reattaching the hand to the arm.

The first step of the herculean task was to clean the jagged tears of the hand and forearm. Surgeons removed some damaged tissue including seven wrist bones that had been crushed in the accident. Then an eight-inch metal rod was inserted between the arm and hand to hold the two together. One end was inserted into one of the two forearm bones, while the other was fastened to the bone of the middle finger.

Next the blood vessels were reconnected. Arteries, which bring blood into the hand, were sutured. Two of the veins presented some difficulty because they had been torn so badly that they could not be directly connected. The solution was to remove four-inch venal sections from Renee's foot and then bridge these between the torn sections of arm and hand veins. As circulation resumed, the hand became pink and warm, the final indicator of vital tissue.

Though circulation and appearance had been restored, the doctors' job was far from complete. Surgeons reconnected the intricate tendons necessary for movement. Nerves and their branches were tackled next. Renee's thumb required repair, because the nail and skin had been ripped free. The thigh area served as a donor for the skin used for covering the thumb as well as for the back of the hand.

In the months since the original operation, doctors have been cautious about predicting Renee's future. Some feel the operation has not restored enough dexterity to the hand for her to become a classical flutist. With extensive physical therapy, however, Renee Katz may at least one day play the flute again, as she vowed from her hospital bed. Not long ago, such an event would have been unthinkable.

It must be pointed out that in cases like these, microsurgery is used along with standard surgery. The doctor may switch from one to the other as the occasion demands. Microsurgery expands the surgeon's capabilities, but it is not the solution in every case. "Clean" amputations that involve the slicing of a body part are more suited to microsurgery's techniques than torn or mangled parts. For instance, after doctors at the Veteran's Administration Hospital in Syracuse evaluated the case of a man who had two fingers torn off, they decided that reattachment was not appropriate because nerve damage was too extensive.

One of the most important digits that doctors recommend be replanted, if at all possible, is the thumb. This digit allows the hand to grasp objects. When the thumb has been so badly crushed that reattachment is not possible, a substitute is available. American doctors have adopted the Chinese technique of removing a big toe and sewing it to the thumb socket. The appearance is surprisingly normal. The invented digit has been coined a "thoe" by Dr. Joseph Upton of the Children's Hospital Medical Center in Boston. Many medical centers now do the toe-to-thumb transformation with a high success rate.

The concept of swapping parts is being extended to other areas of the body as well. In China, a train accident severed a man's left foot as well as causing extensive damage to the left calf and right foot. When doctors realized there was no hope of saving either the left calf or the right foot, they took an unusual course of action. They attached the left foot to the right leg, thus assuring that the patient would have one complete leg. The other side was outfitted with an artificial limb, and he now walks without crutches.

Microsurgeons accomplished another unique rearrangement of body tissue on a motorcycle accident victim in upstate New York's capital district. When David Cruickshank of Clifton Park lost his right foot, doctors feared that amputation at a higher level might be necessary because the lower leg's bones protruded through the open wound, inviting constant infection. David came to St. Peter's Hospital in Albany where he became the area's first successful microsurgery patient. On April 24, 1980, a team headed by Dr. Gerald Colman used fresh tissue to resurface the exposed bone of Cruickshank's lower leg. Then muscle and skin were removed from the patient's back and molded into a simulated foot. Tiny arteries in the muscle were carefully dissected and sewn to compatible arteries in the leg. The operation began at 7:30 A.M. and ended at 11:00 that evening. Today the patient is able to walk with his newly-constructed foot.

After ten days, doctors can usually make an accurate prognosis for patients with reattached or substituted body parts. If the part endures this initial period, then there is a good chance the survival will be permanent. Even though circulation is restored immediately, the total mending process occurs over the next several months. Tendons require a month of healing. Bones are slower and need at least two months to complete their growth. The time involved for a nerve to renew itself varies depending on the distance it must cover; this tissue grows at the rate of an inch per month. When a finger has been reattached, six months may elapse before function and sensation return to the digit. An entire limb would take even longer.

A restored part rarely achieves the same level of dexterity that it had before the accident. Dr. Rollin Daniel of Royal Victoria Hospital in Montreal explains, "I always tell my patients that the replanted limb or digit will never be completely normal again. There's just no way of really predicting how well a reattached limb or digit will work." An arm that has been replanted may end up shorter than the original. A finger tip may lack the keen sensation it once possessed. In all cases, however, the patient knows that it is much easier to live with the inconvenience than without the part.

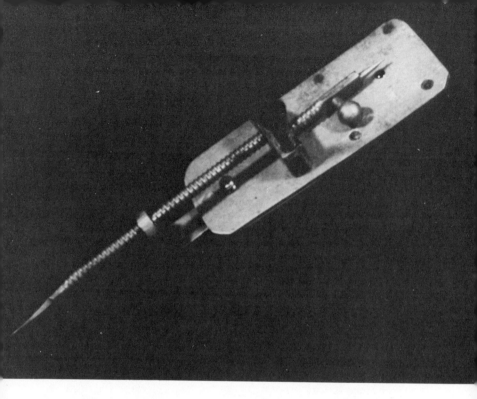

ABOVE AND BELOW: *Replica of Leeuwenhoek's "paddle" microscope (circa 1680). Although not the inventor of the microscope, Leeuwenhoek is considered the "father of microscopy" because he was the first to publish observations of microscopic specimens.* COURTESY ONTARIO SCIENCE CENTRE

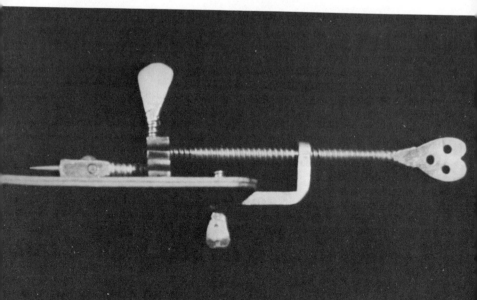

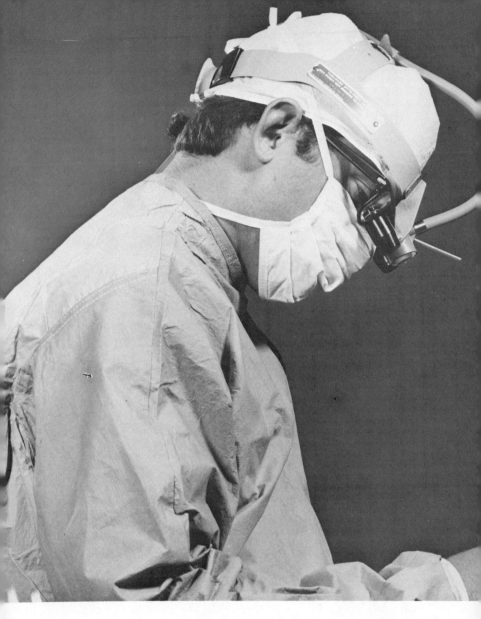

This microsurgeon is wearing a pair of eyeglasses fitted with optical loupes. (Text page 29)

COURTESY DESIGNS FOR VISION, INC.

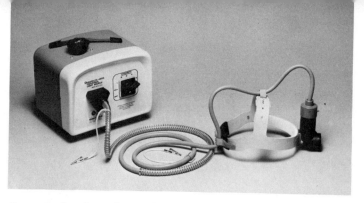

Separate headgear beams light in the direction of the microsurgeon's gaze. This apparatus is used with optical loupes. (Text page 29)
COURTESY DESIGNS FOR VISION, INC.

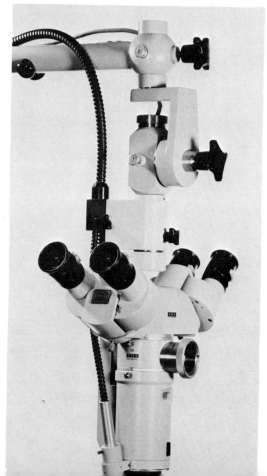

Microscope with twin viewing heads permits an assistant or observer to share the view.
(Text page 30)
COURTESY CARL ZEISS , INC., NEW YORK

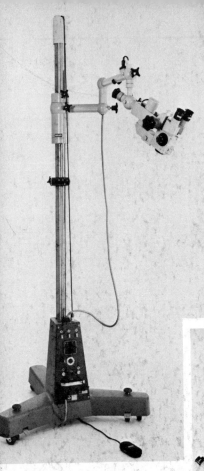

Neurosurgery microscope on floorstand.
COURTESY CARL ZEISS , INC.,
NEW YORK

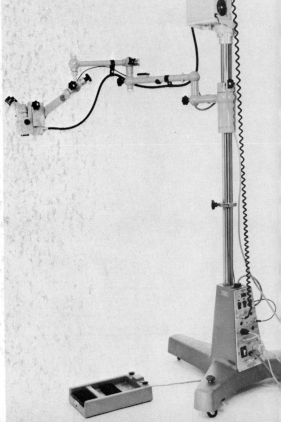

Operation microscope for ophthalmology. Extension arms permit free positioning of lenses over the operation site. Note foot controls. (Text page 29)
COURTESY CARL ZEISS , INC.,
NEW YORK

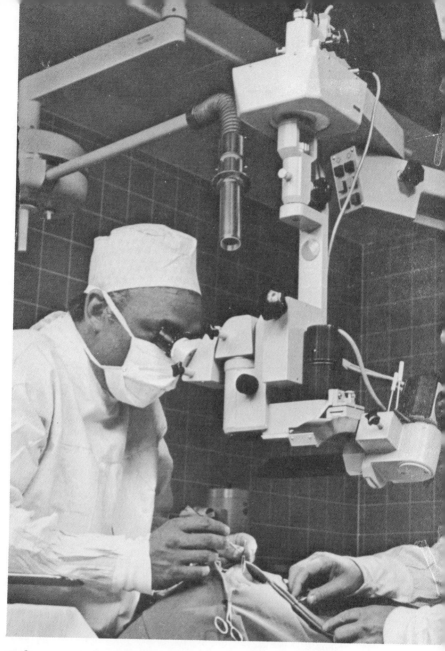

Ceiling-mounted units help unclutter the usually crowded floorspace of the operating room. Note the microsurgeon's right arm braced against an armrest.

COURTESY CARL ZEISS , INC. , NEW YORK

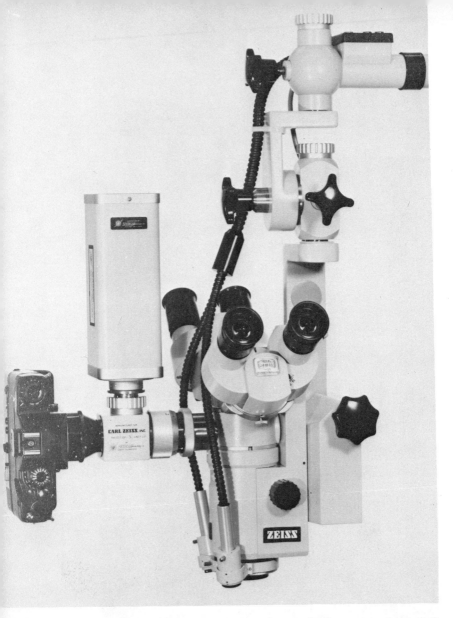

Television and 35mm cameras attached to microscope unit permit close-up documentation of the operation. Second-hand witnesses see the same crisp view as the surgeon. (Text page 31)

COURTESY CARL ZEISS , INC. ,NEW YORK

Curved needles help control the depth of cut when stitching tissue. The microsurgeon manipulates the needle with a pair of forceps. (Text page 32) COURTESY XOMED INC.

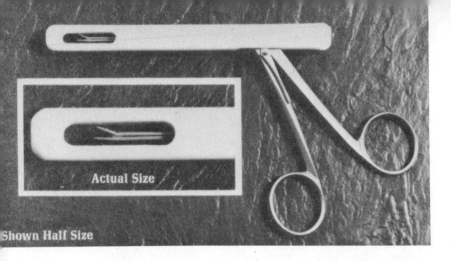

Actual Size

Shown Half Size

Instrument guard protects the delicate tips of alligator forceps. (Text page 32)

COURTESY XOMED INC.

Miniature power tools, such as this lightweight micro-drill, provide quick surgical removal of bone. The narrow shank does not obstruct the view. (Text page 32)

COURTESY XOMED INC.

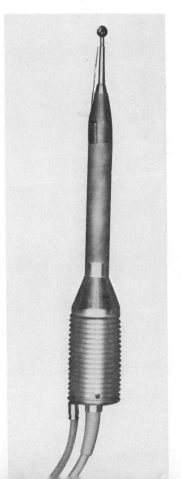

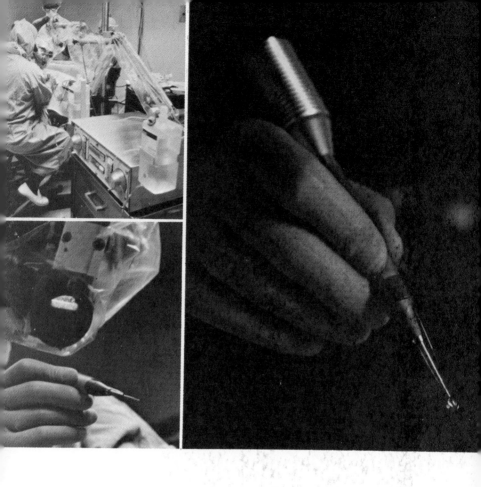

Miniature power tools, such as this lightweight micro-drill, pro-vide quick surgical removal of bone. The narrow shank does not obstruct the view. (Text page 32)   COURTESY XOMED INC.

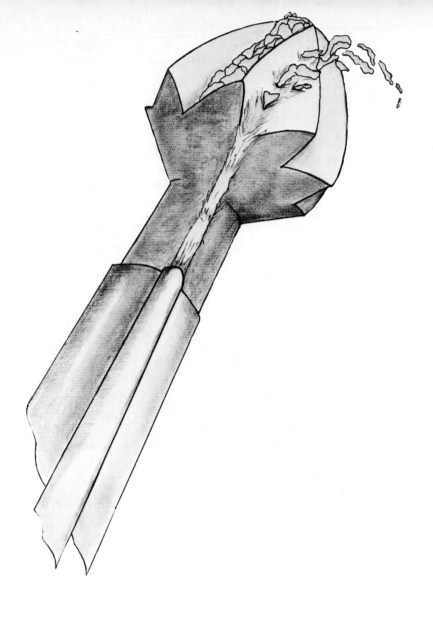

*A built-in irrigation system for the micro-drill washes away
debris from the bit. (Text page 32)* COURTESY XOMED INC.

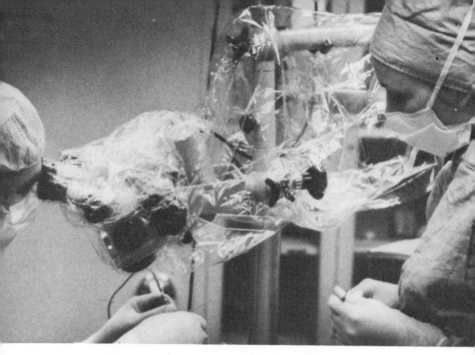

The entire microscope unit is covered with sterile, disposable plastic to ensure sterility. The barrier does not need to be broken because adjustments are remote controlled. (Text page 35)

COURTESY XOMED INC.

Isolation drapes encase the patient in sterile plastic to guard against infection. (Text page 35)

COURTESY XOMED INC.

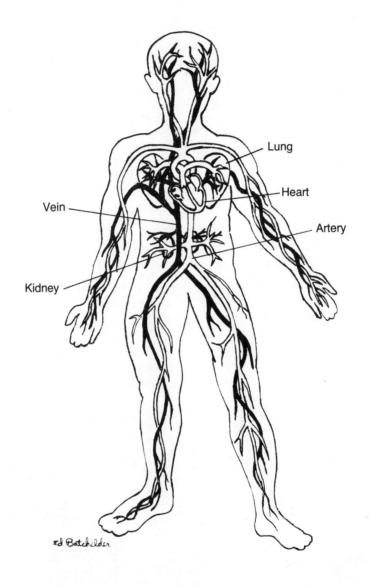

Lung

Heart

Vein

Artery

Kidney

Ed Batchelder

CARDIOVASCULAR SYSTEM *(Text pages 36–43, 100)*

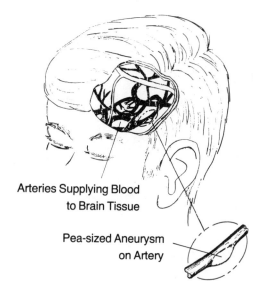

ANEURYSM

(Text pages 38, 77–78)

Arteries Supplying Blood
to Brain Tissue

Pea-sized Aneurysm
on Artery

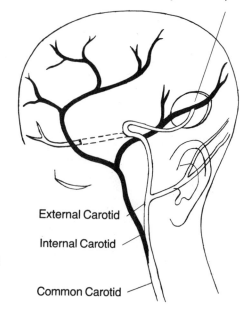

Re-Routed Carotid Artery from Temple

External Carotid

Internal Carotid

Common Carotid

CAROTID ARTERY

(Text pages 41–43, 107)

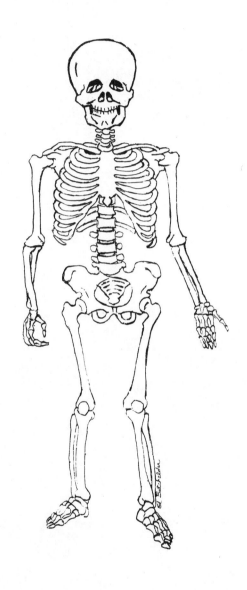

SKELETAL SYSTEM *(Text pages 45–47)*

TYPICAL OPPOSING MUSCLES

(Text page 46)

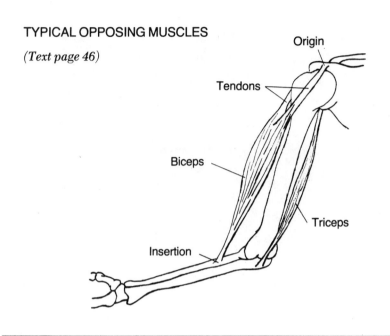

Origin

Tendons

Biceps

Triceps

Insertion

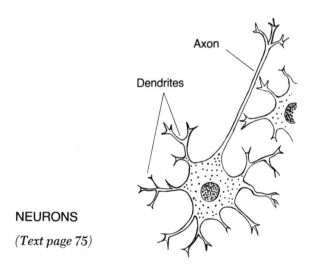

Axon

Dendrites

NEURONS

(Text page 75)

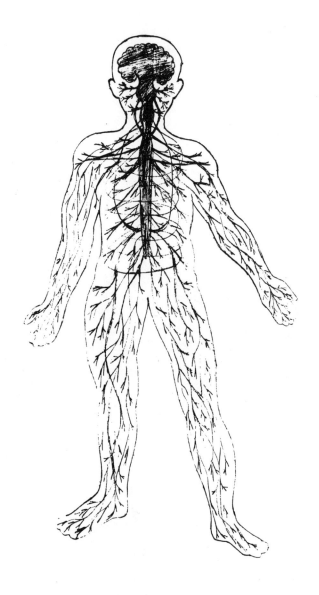

CENTRAL NERVOUS SYSTEM *(Text pages 74–81)*

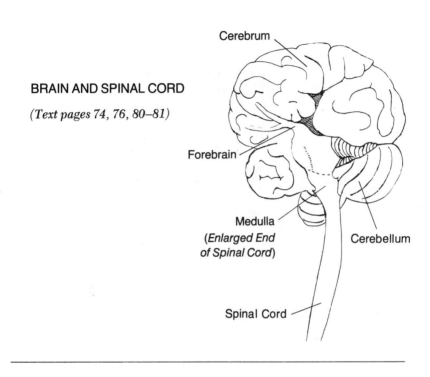

BRAIN AND SPINAL CORD

(Text pages 74, 76, 80–81)

Cerebrum

Forebrain

Medulla
*(Enlarged End
of Spinal Cord)*

Cerebellum

Spinal Cord

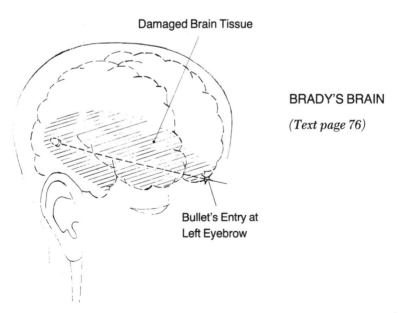

Damaged Brain Tissue

BRADY'S BRAIN

(Text page 76)

Bullet's Entry at
Left Eyebrow

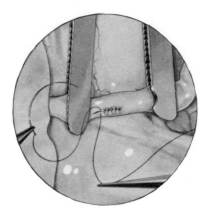

In most vascular surgery, clamps are used to steady the vessel as well as exclude blood during the stitching process. (Text page 78)

COURTESY DESIGNS FOR VISION, INC.

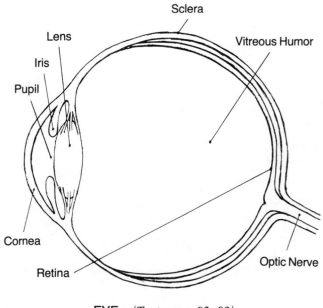

EYE   *(Text pages 82–83)*

MYOPIC EYE *(Text pages 86–88)*

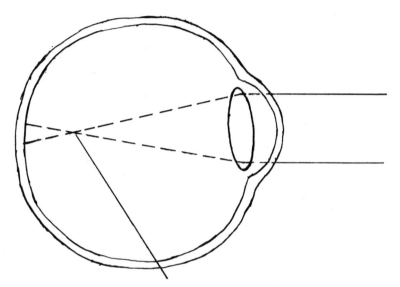

Image Falls Short of Retina

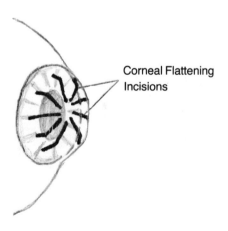

Corneal Flattening
Incisions

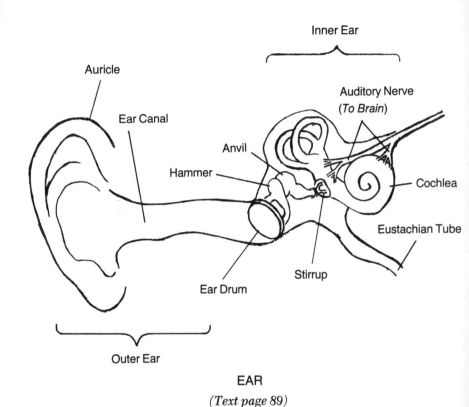

EAR

(Text page 89)

Miniature stainless steel prosthesis is used to replace the stirrup of the middle ear. (Text page 90) COURTESY XOMED INC.

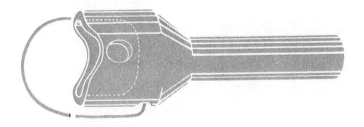

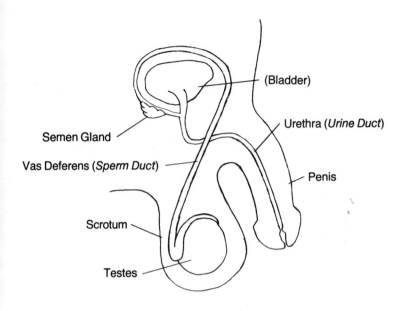

(Bladder)

Urethra (*Urine Duct*)

Penis

Semen Gland

Vas Deferens (*Sperm Duct*)

Scrotum

Testes

MALE REPRODUCTIVE SYSTEM
(Text pages 92–93)

FEMALE REPRODUCTIVE SYSTEM
(Text pages 93–94)

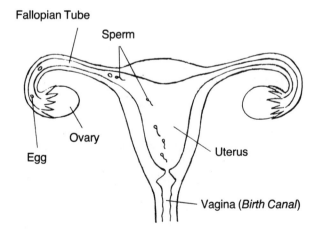

Fallopian Tube

Sperm

Ovary

Egg

Uterus

Vagina (*Birth Canal*)

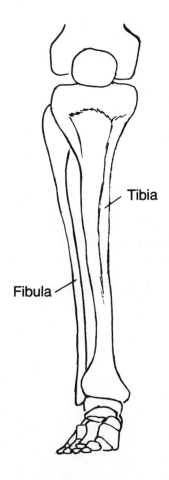

Tibia

Fibula

LOWER LEG BONES

(Text page 101)

Porous man-made materials may be implanted in the body when rebuilding damaged structures. The body's natural tissues grow into the material. (Text page 103)

COURTESY XOMED INC.

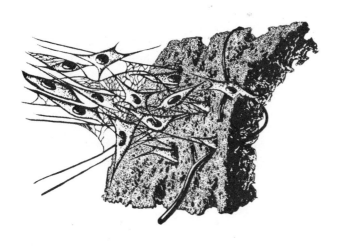

6
Neurosurgery

One part of the human anatomy truly being explored as a new frontier as a result of the advances in microsurgery is the nervous system. Operations that previously would not even be attempted are now being performed with incredible success. The deep folds of the brain have literally opened before the microsurgeon's probing eyes.

The nervous system is composed of the brain, the spinal cord, and the nerves. This trio is the master control system for all bodily functions, keeping everything running smoothly at all times. When changes in the internal or external environment occur, the nervous system senses them and makes any necessary adjustments. Simpler life forms also contain nervous systems, but not as specialized as the human counterpart. Jellyfish, for example, have a net-like group of sensors spread over their entire body. As creatures became more biologically complex through the ages and were faced with new sources and kinds of stimuli, their nervous systems correspondingly grew more sophisticated. A worm, for instance, contains a mass of nerves at one end of its body, which constitutes a brain in the elementary sense of the term: it reacts, but without thoughts. Mammals developed larger brains to cope with added sensory stimuli such as sight and sound. Further, their brains regulated functions like temperature and balance.

Nerve cells, or neurons, are the building blocks of the nervous system. Each neuron typically has a central body with several short, root-like branches called dendrites and one long extension called an axon. Transmission of messages through the nervous system involves small electrical charges that originate from chemical reactions within the nerve cell. The axon portion of a neuron transmits a signal, and then the neighboring dendrite of another cell receives it.

Neurons are capable of astounding speeds in the generation and transmission of impulses. Each cell can send up to one thousand charges—traveling as fast as two hundred miles per hour—in a single second. The twelve billion nerve cells in the body are generally grouped into bundles of cells called, collectively, nerves. These nerves have a white color, whereas collections of neuron bodies are gray. Since nerves are soft and vulnerable, they are packed within the protective tissue of muscle or bone.

There are several levels of functions performed by the human nervous system, each involving different structures. The lowest level of response—like that of the worm—is a direct, spontaneous reaction or reflex, which involves the spinal cord and requires no thought process. Touching a hot object, for example, causes sensory nerves in the skin to send an impulse to the spinal cord, which immediately sends a message to the biceps muscle. The muscle contracts, and the arm pulls back.

The next level of human nervous function, involuntary

action, requires no conscious thought either. Structures at the base of the brain, including the enlarged end of the spinal cord, govern one's breathing, heartbeat, salivation, and so on. Muscle coordination and balance also receive commands from this area. Seated within the center of the brain is the forebrain. This is responsible for creating basic emotions like fear, anger, and sexual urges.

The uppermost part of the brain, and by far the largest, is the cerebrum, which makes up three-fourths of the brain's total three-pound weight. It is the center of all thought and is responsible for memory, reasoning, speech, and voluntary control of the muscles. The cerebrum is divided into halves. Since the nerve impulses that initiate muscular contraction cross over in the spinal cord, the right half controls movements on the left side of the body, and vice versa.

This cerebrum division, coupled with the techniques of microsurgery, played a major role in the incredible recovery story of James S. Brady, the White House Press Secretary who was shot in the brain during a March 30, 1981, assassination attempt on President Reagan. A stray bullet pierced Brady's left eyebrow, passed through the right hemisphere of the cerebrum, and stopped near the right ear. So critical was the wound that doctors first gave little hope for his survival, and television coverage had actually reported him as dead.

But Brady was fortunate the bullet traveled in the direction it did. Had its path been reversed, the left side of his brain would have been damaged, destroying the areas associated with speech and thinking, and affecting motor functions on the right side of the body. Right-handed James Brady might have survived, but he would never be able to function in any significant sense.

Within minutes of the shooting, a team of four microsurgeons headed by Dr. Arthur I. Kobrine hovered over Brady in the operating room. Wearing magnifying loupes, their first priority was to halt the bleeding from two brain arteries. Next they removed dead brain tissue, the bullet, and tiny bone scraps. During the operation, the neurosurgeons tried to keep live brain tissue intact; they particularly avoided contact with the left side of the brain as much as possible so no additional loss of function would be accidentally inflicted.

As this book is being written, Brady is still not home free, but his speech, memory, vision, and hearing are normal. He is alert and jokes with his doctors who predict that forty-year-old Brady will probably limp and need to keep his left arm in a sling, a small price to pay for a life whose chance for survival had been considered minimal.

The tremendous impact microsurgery is having on brain surgery affects thousands of the not-so-famous as well. A brain aneurysm, a weakness in the wall of an artery supplying blood to the brain tissue, is particularly dangerous because the puffed-out side can leak blood or even burst, causing massive hemorrhaging. Traditional surgical methods had often proven to be as unsafe as the diseased condition itself, especially when the aneurysm was imbedded in a hard-to-reach spot. A recent study by Johns Hopkins neurosurgeons in Baltimore has shown that patients with brain aneurysms had only a fifty-percent chance of surviving the operation. Since the implementation of microsurgery in dealing with brain aneurysms, that rate has jumped to ninety percent. Dr. Donlin Long remarks that, "Few things in medicine in the recent past have had that kind of impact on mortality."

There are two basic approaches used in safely ridding the

artery of the pea-sized aneurysm: one involves positioning a miniature titanium clip at the base of the bulge, completely sealing the aneurysm from the wall of the flickering pink artery, while still allowing a continuous flow of blood through the vessel. The aneurysm is then pricked so it collapses, the incision in the head is resewn and the operation is complete. The clip remains attached to the vessel where it keeps the weak area pinched together but otherwise has no effect on the patient. This method would be preferred in cases where the artery wall is extremely weak, so the clip can provide reinforcement. The second approach to removing aneurysms is to snip away the aneurysm after the clip is in place and repair the gap by stitching the walls back together. Then the clip is removed.

Either method requires a slow, meticulous approach. Pitfalls in performing the operation can be numerous. If an aneurysm is clipped too closely to its head, it could rupture and spew blood from the opening, leading to almost certain death for the patient. At the other extreme, if the functioning artery itself is pinched, blood flow could be blocked, which would lead to a stroke and paralysis. The microsurgeon must exercise precise skill and hit the crucial bull's-eye on his target: This marksman only gets one shot.

Aneurysms are not the only structures that have been made more accessible by microsurgery. The pituitary gland, buried in the brain, is responsible for secreting hormones that control the basic body functions, like growth. Although tumors of the pituitary might only measure an eighth-of-an-inch in diameter, they can be disastrous, even fatal. They account for ten percent of all brain tumors, and no satisfactory treatment had been devised until microsurgery came along. Radiation and hormone therapy only provided spotty success; conventional surgery was extremely hazardous because the route of incision was through the top of the head, where the surgeon risked hitting the optic nerve lying directly above the pituitary gland. Damage to the nerve could result in blindness.

The new microsurgical techniques now allow surgeons to reach the pituitary from a position behind the nose. The first step in such a procedure is to make an incision in the gum tissue above the upper row of teeth. The patient's face is pushed up and some of the nose cartilage removed. A hole is cut through the thin bone of the exposed sinus cavity to reveal the pituitary lying on the opposite side. The surgeon is then able to excise the tumor from the gland and sear the site with alcohol to prevent re-growth. Another advantage of this procedure, besides its high success rate, is that no external scar is left.

The repair of nerves is another new field opened through microsurgery. Nerves are no thicker than pencil lead, and their multiple strands can be compared to the separate wires within a telephone cable, each component having its own function. When a nerve is cut, the reconnection procedure must match up the individual fibers. In the past, surgeons had to allow fate to determine how many of the fibers would align themselves correctly. Statistically, this hit-or-miss method produced poor results; only twenty percent of the rejoined nerves gained function. Unfortunately, even with microsurgery it is difficult to tell the fibers apart, and occasionally a wire gets crossed, but the ability to sew nerves back together has been a big factor in the success of replantation operations. Keeping an arm alive by returning circulation to the tissue is one matter, but the restoration of usefulness to the limb requires delicate nerve repair so that the muscles can be properly controlled by their owner. When the ends of two nerves cannot be stitched directly, it is sometimes possible to splice in a nerve section taken from another part of the body. Microsurgeons also have the capability of transplanting nerves from area to area. In the case of a paralyzed facial muscle, for example, a patient might recoup animation by substituting a nerve from the opposite side of the face.

While microsurgery is helping some surgeons rejoin nerves, it seems paradoxical that other surgeons are using the same technology to cut them. This is the case, however, in the remedy for a condition known as tic douloureux in which the sufferer experiences jabbing pain flashes in the face. The disease has been known for almost two thousand years since it was first identified by a Greek physician.

The cause of the agonizing spasms, which can be triggered by even a slight draft to the area, is the trigeminal nerve. Up to the advent of microsurgery, the only treatment was to cut the trigeminal. This put a stop to all pain, but caused the loss of sensation on the face. Another potentially serious side effect was the loss of the corneal reflex, responsible for the production of germ-killing tears and the blinking of eyelids whenever a foreign object enters the eye. The eye thus becomes open to infection and damage without this defense.

Neurosurgeons Dr. Robert W. Rand of the University of California at Los Angeles and Dr. Peter J. Jannetta of Louisiana State University discovered that a group of fibers within the trigeminal nerve actually cause the intense pain. The spasms of tic douloureux occur when the fibers become compressed by blood vessels. With the aid of the microscope, the surgeon can identify by their position the affected trigeminal nerve strands and snip those that cause the pain. The other fibers responsible for normal sensation and the corneal reflex are left intact.

If a microsurgeon isn't rejoining, transplanting or cutting nerves, he may be untangling them. A promising new treatment is emerging for spina bifida, the second most common birth defect—chromosomal anomalies, such as Down's Syndrome, are the most common. Known as "open spine," spina bifida involves the spinal column, where a pouch-like growth containing fluid and nerves causes paralysis below its point of development. Doctors are now able to separate the nerves from the sac and preserve them with the hope of restoring function. The exposed sac is then removed without having destroyed the vital nerve tissue.

Other disorders of the spinal cord are also benefiting from microsurgery. When blood vessels grow abnormally in the spinal cord, they can actually rob the nerves of vital oxygen and nutrients. As a result, the patient might become weak and clumsy or even paralyzed. Prior to microsurgery, the ailment was left untreated; there was nothing that medical practitioners could do to relieve it. Now surgeons can use the techniques of microsurgery to see the blood vessels, sort them out, and destroy them. In many cases the spinal cord resumes the normal prediseased state.

Computer programmers know that the systems they develop are only as good as the data fed into the machine. The same is true with the computer network of brain, spinal cord, and nerves that keeps the human body running efficiently; input to the nervous system comes through the sensory organs where microsurgery is also being applied with amazing success.

7
The Better to See and Hear You

The most developed human sense is vision. The eye is responsible for funneling a tremendous amount of data into the brain for interpretation. The eye is well-protected by its recessed position in a bony socket, so very little of its surface is exposed. Whenever conditions threaten the eye, the eye-lid squeezes closed to shut out the intruder.

The structure of the eye is spherical, its size about the same as a Ping-Pong ball. Filled with a clear jelly called vitreous humor, the eye is covered by a strong, thin sac— this is the white of the eye—and is known as the sclera.

The cornea, a transparent tissue at the front of the eye, admits light to the interior by gathering rays and focusing them. Just inside the cornea lie the pupil and iris. The pupil is nothing more than the hole, surrounded by the iris' ringed curtain of tissue, which opens and closes automatically in response to light conditions. In dim light, a set of tiny muscles tug the iris toward its outer circumference, thus exposing a larger opening and allowing more light to enter. The opposite reaction occurs in bright light; and the iris closes down to restrict the opening.

The lens, lying behind the iris and pupil, directs the incoming light onto the eye's rear wall. Muscles attached to the lens control its shape so that near or distant objects can be focused upon. An area about the size of a postage stamp known as the retina contains many imbedded light-sensitive nerve endings. Stimulated cells convert light into nerve impulses, which are sent directly to the brain by the optic nerve. The brain translates these electrical signals into sight in an interesting way. Groups of nerve fibers from each eye's left half are connected to the brain's left side, and those from the right half of each eye are attached to the right side of the brain. Thus the brain only receives half of the total image from each of its sides. This arrangement provides us with the depth perception needed to place things in perspective.

The area of the retina that lies directly opposite the lens has a particularly high concentration of sensors, enabling the eye to record a very sharp, clear image. In contrast, the small oval point at which the optic nerve is attached has no sensors and does not register any light patterns at all.

One of the first applications of the operating microscope was to eye surgery, and recent advances in technique have expanded this area even further. Cataracts, one of the leading causes of blindness, is a disease where the lens grows cloudy and produces shadowy vision. Microsurgery has enabled ophthalmologists to remove the affected lens more easily. In 1970, the average hospital stay for a cataract patient was ten days; three long months passed before he or she was able to function. By 1975, improvements in technology permitted doctors to do cataract surgery on an outpatient basis and the patient was ready to resume normal activities immediately.

After the eye's natural lens is removed surgically, the organ is left without corrective power to properly focus the incoming light rays onto the retina. This capability is usually restored by contact lenses or thick cataract glasses. Now an alternative has been made available by a microsurgical procedure developed by Dr. Jose Barraquer of Bogota, Colombia. Called refractive keratoplasty, the operation involves implanting an insert made of living tissue into the patient's own eye. The tissue is obtained from a donor eye, possibly a fatal accident victim who had previously made a bequest to donate his body parts to anyone in need of them.

The surgeon slices the cornea from the donor eye and places it onto a cryolathe, a machine that grinds the tissue, which has been frozen after extraction from the donor, to exact specifications in much the same way that contact lenses are ground. The circular piece is then dyed a bright, nonpermanent color for visibility during the operation. With these initial preparations out of the way, the patient is brought into the operating room and anesthetized. To keep the eye wide open, a wire brace is placed over the head, and then a metal ring is fitted onto the eyeball itself. The surgeon then goes to work with an electronic knife, which he slowly moves over tracks in the metal ring, slicing off a thin corneal layer.

Peering through a microscope, the doctor aligns the slice in its original position and loosely sutures it back in place. Then he sandwiches the newly manufactured lens between the patient's two layers of cornea. After the thread is pulled tight, the split cornea molds itself around the insert, forming a substitute lens. The eyelid is sewn shut for two days to prevent the patient from squeezing or rubbing the eye, actions which might force the lens out.

Although keratoplasty has been used successfully to correct the vision of extremely near- or far-sighted individuals, to date, in the United States, it has almost exclusively been used in cataract procedures.

For the majority of cataract victims, a donor eye is not always readily available. As a result of microsurgery another option is available. Intraocular lens implants are performed at the time of cataract surgery when the diseased natural lens is removed. Then, the microsurgeon inserts a tiny clear plastic disk which can remain in the eye permanently. Unlike the keratoplasty operation, which places the correction at the front of the eye in the cornea, intraocular implants replace the lens within the eye.

More than 175,000 eyes have undergone the operation—now so simple it can even be done in the patient's home. Once data about short- and long-term risks are evaluated, the anticipated formal approval from the Food and Drug Administration will increase this figure sharply. Ophthalmologist Dr. Miles A. Galin of New York Medical College cites the implants' benefits. "An intraocular lens implant puts the patient back physiologically to where he was before his cataract ever formed. Understand, these implants are not for everyone, but with the correct case and an appropriately trained surgeon, they represent a major advance."

While cataracts primarily strike the elderly, other forms of eye diseases are certainly not limited to this group. Microsurgery has been used over the entire spectrum of age. On January 23, 1981, in Atlantic City, New Jersey, Sabrina Richardson gave birth to a baby girl whose left cornea was so weak it threatened to rupture and leak the eye's contents. Corneal transplants are usually not performed on newborn infants; doctors wait until the child is one or two years of age. But newborn Jamie Richardson's situation was so critical it demanded immediate action.

At the tender age of one week, Jamie was transferred to St. Christopher's Hospital in Philadelphia. Dr. Joseph Kubacki performed a corneal transplant using tissue from the donated eye of a nine-year-old girl killed in an auto accident. Young corneas are much better in transplant cases on children, because the newer, unaged tissue is more likely to remain clear during the recipient's lifetime. After surgeons cut the cornea to fit the baby's eye, Dr. Kubacki spent three hours behind the microscope. He says the chances for the transplant's success are good, because the blood flow to this area of the body is light, and this reduces the risk of tissue rejection, a factor in many transplants from outside sources.

The operation, however, did not correct Jamie's sight. Her vision cannot be tested because of her age, and it is likely that future operations will be necessary because the lenses in both eyes are malformed. The right eye's cornea is dangerously weak, too. What the microsurgical procedure accomplished was to save the eye.

An operation about which people might have second thoughts is a new microsurgical procedure called radial keratotomy. Designed to correct nearsightedness, it is currently the center of a major controversy. Opponents, such as the National Advisory Eye Council, wish to see more scientific studies to help determine the safety and effectiveness of the operation. They claim that the experimental technique could develop into a billion-dollar-a-year industry even though enough time has not yet elapsed to assess its long-term effects. The government group is not against technology that could help cure eye defects; they simply wish to discourage the premature proliferation of the procedure.

Approximately one-third of all Americans suffer from nearsightedness, or myopia. The cause of their blurred vision is an eyeball that is too long. For sharpest vision, an image should fall directly on the retina, but the nearsighted person's image falls short of the retina when he or she tries to see something in the distance. Usually this situation can be corrected with glasses or contact lenses. In 1973, another method to force the image onto the retina was accidentally discovered in the Soviet Union, when a myopic sixteen-year-old boy got into a fight and broke his glasses. In the scuffle his cornea was cut. As the wound healed, the cornea reshaped itself to provide the boy with perfect vision in that eye. This amazing finding led Russian ophthalmologist Svyatoslav Fyodorov to experiment with surgical inducement of the same effect.

By mid-1981 over two thousand such operations had been performed in the United States. Taking only fifteen minutes, the steps involved are relatively simple and can be done as an outpatient procedure in a hospital or doctor's office with only eyedrops used for anesthesia. While looking through a microscope, the surgeon uses a blade guarded by a metal disk on top of the cornea to make sixteen incisions in a spoke-like pattern. The cuts extend from the iris outward but are not placed in the center where the pupil admits light into the eye. As the eye heals, the curvature of the cornea flattens slightly, refocusing the image closer to the retina. The recovery period is forty-eight hours, during which there may be some minor discomfort and redness.

In theory, radial keratotomy seems to be the answer for the millions of people who would like to cast off their glasses forever. But the National Advisory Eye Council, the leading United States government advisory group concerned with vision research, urges ophthalmologists and near-sighted people to exercise restraint until more systematic research has been undertaken. Not everyone who under-goes the expense of $1,500 or more per eye will receive an absolute cure. It is common for vision to regress from twen-ty to twenty-five percent during the first three months following surgery. For this reason, microsurgeons try to overshoot the figure when calculating the placement and depth of the cuts. Many of the patients, however, still need to wear some form of corrective lenses after the operation, although they are now less powerful. "After a radial kerato-tomy, about fifty-five percent of the patients function with-out glasses and the remaining forty-five percent have some degree of improvement," reported *The New York Times*. Other patients notice that their vision is sharpest in the morning and then blurs throughout the day. And, night-time glare becomes bothersome to some because of the scattering of light through the surgical scars.

Despite these present drawbacks, the radial keratotomy holds value for those people who desire it for other than cosmetic reasons. Surgical correction of nearsightedness can make a career as an athlete, pilot, or astronaut accessi-ble to someone who would ordinarily be prohibited from entering the field because of his or her need for glasses. It is unlikely that radial keratotomies will sweep the nation, but their prudent use will continue to be part of the long list of benefits that microsurgery offers.

Until recently, persons suffering from diabetes have had a gloomy future, but a new microsurgery procedure is changing this outlook drastically. In their later years, dia-betics frequently go blind because the vitreous humor, the fluid in the center of the eye, turns cloudy from the bloody debris that collects as a result of rupturing blood vessels.

Surgeons attempt to correct this problem by performing an operation termed a vitrectomy: inserting a tiny probe into the side of the eye. The instrument pierces the outer membrane and withdraws the murky fluid, replacing it with a clear synthetic substitute. The results are sometimes disappointing, but many patients have enough vision restored so that they can move about without help. Several cases have been so successful that the patient is once again able to read. As with any type of elective surgery, there are considerable hazards involved with a vitrectomy that one must balance against the advantages. Infection is a problem; cataracts that might later develop are another. These are risks, however, that are usually outweighed by the possibility of being able to see once again.

Other forms of blindness involve the retina, now yielding too to the wonders of microsurgery. Prior to its new tools and techniques, operating on the rear portion of the eye was unthinkable. Now ophthalmologists can fix a retina that has become detached from the membranes at the back of the eye. In another kind of operation, a layer of vision-robbing disease scar cells on the surface of the retina can be peeled away like an onion's skin. This surgery also extends to correct other sensory impairments once thought incurable.

No less gratifying than the blind being able to see again is the return of hearing to a deaf person. The phenomenon of sound is a result of vibrations moving through a medium, being received by another, and being translated into a meaningful result. What people call the ear is actually a cartilage flap directing vibrations to the other structures within the ear canal. This cup-shaped tissue, known as the auricle, and the tubular passage which extends from it form the outer ear.

At the end of the ear canal lies the eardrum, a tightly-stretched membrane set into motion at the same frequency as the vibrations that strike it. On the opposite side of the eardrum are the smallest bones in the human body, the hammer, anvil, and stirrup, which are named for their shape. These bones and the eardrum comprise the middle ear. The hammer is directly attached to the eardrum and receives the vibrations, quickly passing them along to the anvil. The anvil then passes them to the stirrup. This unique chaining system helps to deaden excessively loud sounds while magnifying quieter ones. The chain carries the vibrations of loud sounds from beginning to end with the same intensity; quiet sounds are augmented by the receiving link.

The last structure to receive the vibrations is located in the inner ear. The cochlea is a snail shape formed from bone. Its inside passages contain fluid with many hair-like extensions of cells. The cells are connected to the endings of the auditory nerve, which, when stimulated, creates impulses. In the brain, the impulses are finally translated into meaningful sound.

The microscope is now an established tradition in ear surgery with over eighty percent of such operations performed with its assistance. When the bones of the middle ear become rigid from a condition known as otosclerosis, the result is deafness. Microsurgery enables doctors to remove some of the bone and replace it with a more supple and resilient prosthesis, sometimes of synthetic material, which restores almost normal hearing.

Reconstruction of the entire middle ear has been accomplished with success rates up to ninety-five percent. Depending on the individual problem, artificial parts or live tissue may be transplanted. For example, a defective stirrup bone might be replaced by a stainless steel wire.

Deafness stemminf from problems in the more complex inner ear can be helped as a result of recent work by researchers at the University of Florida who have succeeded in replacing the inner ear structures of mice with bones made from Bioglass, a ceramic material immune to attack by the body's built-in rejection-defense system.

A different approach to the correction of inner ear deficiencies has been the development of a totally electronic ear. In 1959, Californian Charles Graser was involved in an accident in which he received severe burns. Massive amounts of streptomycin, administered to ward off infection, destroyed the hair cells in the cochlea, which, in turn, broke the sequence of internal events that leads to the sensation of hearing. Electrical signals could no longer be generated in the auditory nerve, and Graser became deaf.

In 1970, Dr. William House of the Los Angeles Foundation of Otology (currently the Ear Research Institute) implanted the first working model of the electric ear into Graser. After drilling through the tough mastoid bone, behind the right ear, the surgeon attached six platinum electrodes onto the cochlea. Finespun wires leading from the tips pinch-hit for the defunct hair cells. These wires ran to a common coil implanted beneath the skin near the back of the ear. To utilize the system, Graser wore a pair of eyeglass frames fitted with a miniature transmitter in the right earpiece. Sounds picked up by a microphone worn on his chest were sent along a concealed cord to the eyeglasses. Here, the transmitter generated a signal that was picked up by the coil behind the ear. The impulse traveled along the wires to the cochlea where the normal course of action was resumed.

Although the electric ear is not able to distinguish pitch changes in order to make the human voice understood, deaf patients who have received the device are elated at the sounds of school bells, chirping birds, and frying bacon. With some fine tuning, a fully functional bionic ear may one day be a reality.

8
Go Forth and Multiply

Reproduction is essential for the continuation of life, and the human species contains a highly efficient system to meet this need. However, the male and female reproductive organs are complex structures which are occasionally plagued by malfunctions. Microsurgery has found yet another application and has made great strides in returning reproductive capacity to normal in many individuals.

The male testes are responsible for producing sperm. The sperm cells pass through the narrow channel of the sperm duct, or vas deferens, on their way to the semen glands where they are mixed with its secretions. During ejaculation, the fluid is passed through the urethra.

One of the problems that can occur with the male sex organs is that the testes may not properly descend into their protective sac, the scrotum. Males with this condition are sterile because a too high body temperature hinders sperm production. Now the techniques of microsurgery can be used to free the testes, without endangering their function, allowing them to descend thus providing a cooler environment.

The extent of impotence is not known since most men are unwilling to admit their sexual difficulties to their doctors. Until recently, experts in the medical profession believed that the inability to sustain an erection was due to psychological factors. Current research, however, reveals that as many as forty-four percent of impotency cases have physical causes. In 1972 a Czechoslovakian doctor, suspected that circulation in the genital area was a basic factor in an erection. Dr. Milorad Jevtich of Washington, D.C., adopted this theory and devised a simple test to determine deficient blood flow during an erection. He uses a device that measures the intensity of the sound waves in the fingers and compares them with those in the penis. If the test indicates that poor circulation is the problem, Jevtich might perform a revascularization, a bypass operation in which a stomach artery is transplanted to the penis. Thus, the amount of blood to the tissue is increased because it can now flow around the defective artery. Fifty percent of Jevtich's patients regain normal sexual function, but he believes the success rate will rise as more doctors use and refine the surgical technique.

Ironically, in this age of increased demand for better forms of birth control, almost twenty percent of all women have trouble getting pregnant. To understand how infertility can occur one must first look at nature's normal chain of events. The ovary is the structure in which the process begins. Once each month an egg is released by the ovary during ovulation. The egg travels down the fallopian tube (also called the oviduct) where it may unite with, and be fertilized by, a sperm if sexual intercourse has taken place. The fertilized egg continues its journey and lodges in the uterus where it develops.

Damaged or defective fallopian tubes prevent pregnancy by blocking the egg's path. The number of women with blocked tubes has been rising in recent years according to Dr. August Schwenk, the chief of Obstetrics and Gynecology at St. Clare's Hospital in Schenectady, New York. Birth defects, infections in the pelvic and abdominal regions, and surgery (other than sterilization) may all produce tube damage, but Schwenk attributes the increase to social factors. Venereal diseases and the use of intrauterine devices can cause damage to the sensitive reproductive organs. Legal abortions, even those performed in hospitals, may cause infections that render the tubes nonfunctional.

Conventional surgical methods to reopen blocked fallopian tubes have had a very poor success rate—about twenty-five percent. Since the advent of microsurgery, that rate has climbed to as high as sixty percent. Scars and growths around the oviducts resulting from abortion, infections, intrauterine birth-control devices, birth defects, and non-sterilization surgery can be initially detected with a small tube, which has a light and a magnifying lens. The device is passed through an incision in the navel during a procedure termed a laparoscopy. Based on the extent of damage, the microsurgeon decides whether surgical clearing of the tubes is feasible. When it is, the new delicate instruments and fine sutures reduce the possibility of scarring from *this* operation, so that the fallopian tubes do not become blocked again.

Sometimes the tubes are in such bad shape that they may have missing or poorly developed parts. Recent work by

Dr. Alvin M. Siegler of the State University of New York's Downstate Medical Center in Brooklyn has offered hope for such cases. "I expected to open up a blocked fallopian tube," he recalls after one operation, "but what I found was that the blocked tube was connected not to the normal uterus, but to a second, rudimentary uterus about the size of the upper part of my thumb. What was done was to bring the second uterus close to the normal one to reduce the tension and to connect the working tube to the working uterus."

After completing this task, Dr. Siegler saw other possibilities. He believes that sections of two diseased fallopian tubes could be rearranged to produce a single good tube. For example, the unmarred top of one tube may be pieced with the bottom of the other.

While men and women are seeking help for infertility problems, many more have reversed a previous decision about permanent sterilization and are hoping to regain fertility. Voluntary sterilization is the form of contraception chosen by more people worldwide than any other. A total of ten million people in the United States alone have undergone surgery to prevent pregnancy, but, of these, twenty-five to thirty thousand each year decide they do want to have babies.

What factors cause people to change their minds? About half of those requesting reversals do so because they have remarried and now want children with their new spouses. In the case of remarriage after divorce, perhaps one of the partners had undergone a sterilization operation as a desperate attempt to save his or her first marriage; the marriage fails anyway, and now the person regrets that decision. A sudden tragedy may occur in a happily married couple's life. The death of children in a car accident or fire could wipe out an entire family in an instant. An infant runs a high risk of death during the first year of life, and if one of the parents has been sterilized during that period, he or she may seek a reversal should the child die. Sometimes a man has the operation performed while his wife is pregnant, because the couple has decided they don't want any more children. If the pregnancy ends in miscarriage, the man may realize his action was too hasty.

Whatever the reason for the change of heart, microsurgery can come to the rescue. In women, the original operation to sever the fallopian tubes and tie the ends lasts a half hour, at most. The egg produced by the ovaries is thus prevented from following its normal path to the uterus, and is absorbed by surrounding tissue. The net result is permanent sterility. Before microsurgery, attempts to reconnect the tubes often failed. Dr. Sherman Silber of the Ballas Medical Center in St. Louis, and a leader in this area of urology, explains: "The answer for the previous high failure rates lay right under our noses. We just couldn't see it. It wasn't until I began to study the problem under microscopes that I realized we were not achieving the kind of perfect reconnection that was necessary."

The new microsurgical procedure usually takes two to three hours. The surgery is painless and most women stay in the hospital about four days. The biggest factor determining the success of the operation is the way in which the original sterilization was carried out. If large sections of the fallopian tubes were destroyed from excessive cutting or electric cauterizing, then the rejoined tubes will be much shorter. A shorter tube is not able to perform all the functions of the original long tube, thus the egg's chances of being fertilized and implanted in the uterus decrease sharply.

A sterilization technique known as the Pomeroy Method is the easiest to reverse. Although the fallopian tubes are tied after being cut, large portions are not removed and the ends are not sealed by cauterizing. Depending on the patient's possible future need for reversal, metal or plastic clips, which remain in the body, should also be considered by surgeons who perform a sterilization. With clips the tubes are pinched shut, thus any damage is slight and reversal is simplified.

The age of the woman seeking to have a child is another consideration when deciding on reversal. The older the patient, the less chance there is for success. It is not a good idea for women older than thirty-seven to have the operation because problems with the pregnancy or with the baby could occur. A risk that women of any age must face after microsurgical reconnection of the fallopian tubes is the increased possibility of an ectopic pregnancy. Unavoidable scar tissue from the surgery can trap the fertilized egg before it reaches the uterus. Although this is a rare occurrence, another operation would be necessary to scrape the plugged tube. Additional damage could occur, and a normal pregnancy would be even more difficult.

The operation to reverse sterilization costs $3,000 or more, and, of course, pregnancy cannot be guaranteed. But the success rate of around sixty percent is impressive when compared with the seventy-five to eighty percent success rate of healthy women who wish to become impregnated.

The success rate for sterilization reversal in men is even higher—ninety percent. Nearly a million men undergo vasectomies each year. Often costing less than $200, the technique of snipping the vas deferens, the duct which carries sperm from the testis, is a safe, reliable, and convenient means of birth control. The three-hour reverse procedure—a vasovasostomy—is becoming almost as routine, due to microsurgery.

The reversal involves more precise manipulation of tissue than the equivalent operation in women, because the outer diameter of the vas deferens is only an eighth of an inch. An inner vessel which carries the sperm cells can measure as small as one-hundredth of an inch. Under the microscope, the severed ends of this pinpoint-sized tube are joined to form a leak-proof seal. Next, the outer muscular wall is stitched together. The function of this muscular layer is to propel the sperm through the canal by setting up contractions. Any scar tissue from the initial operation is removed at this time to prevent its possible interference in sperm flow.

Requiring only an overnight hospital stay, the vasovasostomy is no more painful than the vasectomy. Sex can begin in two weeks, and normal sperm counts return in three to six months. Although most men who undergo the operation are in their thirties, age is much less of a factor than it is for women. Men in their forties and fifties who have married younger women have no reason to believe that their years will prevent them from becoming new fathers.

The factor that does reduce the chances for fertility is the amount of time that has elapsed since the original vasectomy was performed. When the sperm duct is cut, this leads to a pressure buildup at the end. The production of sperm cells may come to a permanent halt if the condition persists for more than four or five years. Vasectomy reversals attempted after ten years see a sharp drop in their success rate.

In light of the success of microsurgery in obtaining complete reversal of sterilization, will it become an accepted means of temporary birth control? Sterilization is safer than hormones or copper loops and is already more popular with couples who have been married ten years or longer. Higher reversal rates will be possible in the future as recent advances in the sterilization techniques do less damage to the affected tissues. Right now, however, most doctors feel that both men and women should not undergo sterilization unless they are completely sure they will not want children. There are always risks involved in any surgical procedure and most doctors believe it is wise to avoid them if possible.

9
Cancer and Microsurgery

Without a doubt, the disease people most fear is cancer. In the United States, nearly one in four adults gets some form of it, and next to cardiovascular disease it ranks as the second greatest killer in the United States. Although much has been learned about cancer and many forms are now curable, the fear persists.

The disease itself should not be thought of as a single condition. Possessing unique characteristics depending on its location, cancer can strike anywhere in the body. It begins painlessly with a single cell. A virus, a chemical, or radiation induces an abnormal change in the cell which causes it to reproduce wildly, spreading and robbing normal cells of proper nutrition. The chances for curing cancer are best while the diseased tissue remains localized at its initial site. As the disease progresses, the onslaught of cells into adjacent areas occurs. Cancer has reached its advanced stages when the malignant cells have spread to remote tissue through blood or lymph vessels.

The treatments currently being used in the continuing war against cancer are chemotherapy, irradiation, and surgery. Microscopic techniques have expanded the uses and capabilities of surgery. Now with increased access to the cancer, doctors can remove the cancer growth more easily and effectively but the biggest benefit has been in the repair of the ravaged tissue afterwards. Victims of bone cancer often faced amputation of a limb after the disease. A new technique at the Royal Victoria Hospital in Montreal enables the leg to remain intact with a living bone graft. In the late 1970s, in a twelve-hour operation to remove the cancerous section of bone in a twenty-two-year-old woman's right leg, surgeons substituted the fibula—which is not needed for normal support or walking—from the left leg. The operating microscope and delicate instruments allowed doctors to hook up the separate arteries and veins so that blood flow to the graft was established. With a ready supply of nutrients on hand, the transplanted section could grow and mesh with the existing bone.

The aftermath of other types of cancer may require a complete refashioning of a vital body part. In the case of a patient whose cancerous esophagus was removed, facing the gory prospect of having to insert special food through a hole cut in the chest or stomach was a distinct possibility. But microsurgeons were able to preserve the continuity of his digestive tract by removing a section of his intestine and stitching it into his neck. The transplant was made possible because blood vessels could be reconnected under the microscope. Today the man eats normally.

The most common type of cancer affecting American women is breast cancer. Approximately one in eleven women will have the disease at some point in her life. After a radical mastectomy, in which the breast and chest muscles are removed, swelling can occur. The lymph system, responsible for trapping and killing bacteria, continues to secrete fluid. Since the normal drainage channels have been removed in the operation, the fluid is trapped. Some cases have been so severe that the arm balloons to incredible sizes, and amputation becomes necessary when blood poisoning develops. Prevention of this problem can be achieved with microsurgery at the time of the mastectomy by connecting the lymph vessels in the arm to tiny veins. This prevents accumulation of fluid by establishing drainage.

The psychological trauma of breast cancer can be a particularly devastating experience for a woman. She must first deal with the fact that she is fighting cancer. In addition, she faces the loss of a body part when that part is associated by society with feminine attractiveness and sexuality. One of the truly remarkable achievements of modern times is the reconstruction of the breast after a mastectomy, even as late as twenty-five years after the operation. Although most breast reconstruction can be accomplished without a microscope, the techniques of microsurgery have enabled doctors to work on more difficult cases, especially those women who have had radical mastectomies.

Professionals in the medical field once considered attempts to reconstruct a breast too risky, because they feared the spread of cancer. Recent studies, however, have shown that the chance of cancer recurring and spreading is not increased by moving tissue in the area.

A significant factor in the development of breast reconstruction techniques was the number of women who could not view a mastectomy as a permanent handicap that they had to accept. In many instances the quality of their personal and social lives was adversely affected. Strapped-on devices were uncomfortable, irritating, and limited the types of clothing they could wear. The uneven distribution of weight in the device caused back, neck, and shoulder problems. The mastectomy patient who seeks an alternative does so not out of vanity, but as any patient who has lost a limb might. Not surprisingly, with the knowledge that reconstruction can take place afterward, women are better able to deal with the initial prospect of breast removal.

How is the breast reconstructed?

Basically the procedure involves the implantation of a clear, gel-filled prosthesis whose shape resembles the breast. A two- to three-inch incision is made along the crease line where the soon-to-be breast will be inserted. The scar remains practically invisible after the reconstruction. The original scar is not used for this incision, because this might later cause splitting from increased tension on the wound.

Because each woman's breasts vary in size, shape and contour, the operation is different in every case. Also, what was done to the tissue in the mastectomy operation has a direct bearing on how the breast is rebuilt. To restore soft tissues from a radical mastectomy in which the chest muscle is also removed, skin-fat grafts can be placed in the upper chest wall, giving the breast a fuller appearance. The donor site for these grafts is the buttocks area. In other cases, the chest's skin may be tight from the mastectomy, preventing the insertion of an implant beneath it. Additional skin and fatty tissue, and sometimes attached muscle, can be added to the site. Microsurgery plays an integral role in these cases of tissue transfer because the surgeon must connect blood vessels to nourish the area.

When the chest muscle is left intact after the breast's removal, its condition determines whether the implanted pouch will be put over or under it. If the muscle is thin, the implant can be placed beneath it creating soft padding over the sac. Otherwise the implant must be placed on top of the chest muscle and covered with additional tissue.

A missing nipple and its areola (the dark area surrounding the nipple) can also be replaced either during the breast reconstruction operation or at a later time. Skin grafts, tissue from the genital area, or parts of the unremoved breast's nipple may be used in fashioning a new nipple-areola combination. If the original cancer-free nipple was saved at the time the breast was removed, it can now be replanted. However, the safety of this technique is still controversial, and some surgeons will not do it.

If performed, usually when the breast cancer was restricted to an area far from the nipple, a procedure called "nipple banking" is employed. The nipple and areola are separated from the breast during the mastectomy and grafted to a hidden body area, the groin or hip, for example. When reconstruction takes place, the nipple and areola are regrafted to the breast. However, these two successive grafts of the same piece tend to diminish the pigmentation, and healing may not be as complete as when only one transfer is involved. For these reasons, the plastic surgeon may play down the option of saving the nipple and using it again. In any case a brand new nipple can be reconstructed.

The breast reconstruction operation is usually done under general anesthesia. However, if the process requires the insertion of the implant and little rebuilding of other tissues, then local anesthesia might be used. In either situation, there is less pain than when the mastectomy was performed because the deep tissues are affected to a lesser degree. The hospital stay is shorter. Instead of a bandage during the recovery period, the woman wears a specially-fitted snug bra night and day for one month. In addition to serving as a dressing for the wounds, the bra holds the new and old breast in proper alignment as healing takes place, thus preventing slippage of the implant to the side. Healing time varies depending on the extent of work done, but generally the wounds have mended within six months.

Even though surgeons make precise measurements, the placement of the new breast in relation to the existing one is extremely difficult, and perfect symmetry is rarely, if ever, achieved. The chest wall itself is uneven in many cases. The goal of breast reconstruction is a balanced appearance under clothing. Most women can wear bikini swimming suits or go braless under other clothing. The only restriction to choice of style is the location of the mastectomy scars. If the upper part of the breast contains scars, then the woman will have to be more conscious about the selection of low-cut necklines.

Initially, the breast reconstruction patient should exercise her arms slowly, stretching them until there is slight discomfort. Vigorous movements should not be attempted for the first month. After the recovery period, however, she may resume an active lifestyle with no limitations.

Breast reconstruction is a marvelous invention, but the patient should not undertake it blindly. The ideal time to discuss it with the surgeon is before the mastectomy operation. Reconstruction can begin anywhere from three months to many years after the breast is removed. As with any kind of surgery, there are certain risks. Occasionally bleeding or infection can be a problem, and the implant must be removed. Another attempt at reconstruction can be made several months later. In some instances, the body may reject the implant. Sometimes a hard, uncomfortable capsule forms around the implant, because the surrounding tissues have contracted. An additional problem, although rare, is the shifting of the mass until it ends up in a peculiar position. These perils should not prevent a highly-motivated patient from having a breast reconstructed, but she should be aware of them.

The surgeon's fees and hospital costs can range from $2,000 to $10,000, but more and more insurance companies are covering the expense because the operation is no longer classified as cosmetic. Breast reconstruction is an integral part of the rehabilitation process for mastectomy patients.

10
Is It All Good?

There is no denying microsurgery's capacity for accomplishing amazing feats. But anything new is controversial, and microsurgery is no exception. There are positive and negative sides to its use. Its ability to achieve what ordinary surgery cannot sometimes raises ethical concerns.

We have seen how the internal carotid bypass operation has replaced the extremely dangerous use of conventional surgery in one part of the brain. While many risks are diminished by microsurgery, new ones are created, as the tiny tools probe further and further into the delicate areas of the body. A twitch of the hand could cost a life, and it seems that the technique that saves lives makes such slip-ups easier.

The spiraling costs of microsurgery are phenomenal, and there is no end in sight. This is leading some people to carefully balance its costs against its benefits. Young married couples, a group with considerable financial burdens, are frequently faced with a tragic choice when a premature infant is born—lose the baby or go bankrupt. They may believe that every individual from conception onward has the right to life and this view would certainly color their choice; but the cost of caring for the baby can exceed $100,000 if problems arise, and surgery is involved. Within the past ten years the technical advances and the increased number of intensive-care units for the newborn have enabled babies born as many as fifteen weeks prematurely to survive. Even some professionals regard these attempts to preserve life as extraordinary since only thirty percent of the premature infants weighing less than 2.2 pounds at birth survive, and of these, fifteen to twenty-five percent are severely handicapped. In an address to a March of Dimes symposium, Dr. Mitzi L. Duxbury, assistant dean of graduate studies at the University of Minnesota School of Nursing, summed up the situation: "Most parents want and expect normal healthy babies. They don't bargain for a handicapped child and bankruptcy together."

Although microsurgery has raised dozens of fuzzy ethical considerations, there is one concern that it has actually removed. A procedure to surgically relocate an egg from the ovary to the uterus, thus bypassing blocked fallopian tubes, avoids the objections to conception outside the body. Technically, this is not a "test-tube baby" because fertilization occurred by natural means within the body.

Will the demand for microsurgery be so high that it can't be met? It has been estimated that in the United States there are only fifty surgeons who exclusively practice microsurgery. As has happened in the computer field, will the technological advances outstrip the number of qualified personnel available to do the jobs? Could quality suffer as a result of microsurgery's increasingly high demand in the marketplace of health care? These are questions that will not be resolved easily.

A new term—biocommercialism—has already been coined to describe the intermingling of medical progress with economically feasible ventures. In October of 1980, Harvard's administration and faculty were in hot debate over whether the university should invest in a genetic engineering company. The potential to reap huge profit was eventually abandoned because of the conflict it would have created with academic values. It was feared that the school's activities, for example in laboratory research, would be more and more directed toward profit-making ends, rather than strictly adhering to academic interests and the free interchange of ideas. This basic issue will surely surface again in other scientific and medical institutions.

In many instances microsurgery may actually serve to reduce costs by shortening the length of hospital stays and the need for post-operative care. A price tag can never be placed on the benefits that microsurgery is bringing to its patients in terms of improved health and psychic solace. Localized techniques under the microscope minimize the incision requirements for surgery. Who prefers a gaping wound in the body to a small scar?

The very question of who is allowed to have microsurgery is sometimes a touchy matter between patient and doctor. In the case of amputations, patients will usually ask for reattachment. Although possible, the surgeon must decide whether a reattachment would be in the patient's best interest and after careful evaluation will sometimes decide not to reattach the limb. For example, a severed index finger replanted on its owner may restore cosmetic appearance but does little in terms of function. The middle finger quickly assumes the dexterity of the index finger.

The stiff reattached digit then becomes a hindrance and the patient is better off without it. Doctors are compassionate people; they do not want to put a patient through needless surgery and rehabilitation only to have them be disappointed later.

Microsurgery has opened up new possibilities for transplant operations in which donor parts are incorporated into a different recipient's body. What was once a cavalier question now has serious meaning. How much of a person can be replaced before he or she turns into someone else? At the University of Rochester, experimenters raised two sets of rats, one group with diabetes, and the other normal. Then surgeons grafted brain tissue from the normal group to the diabetic rats. The new brains survived, and in many rats the tissue took over regulation of hormone secretion, thus curing the diabetes. Will human brain transplants be performed one day?

Our quality of life has been enhanced by the numerous technological achievements of our space-age society. But is it possible for science to lose sight of its goal of helping people? Has the razzle-dazzle of microsurgery preempted the humanist approach and become an all-consuming monster? We must carefully question whether the object of our attention is people or gadgetry. In a 1980 issue of the *New England Journal of Medicine* an essay titled "Thoughts of a Dying Physician," by 71-year-old cancer victim Dr. Frederick Stenn voiced these concerns during his final days. "Most physicians have lost the pearl that was once an intimate part of medicine—humanism. Machinery, efficiency, precision have driven from the heart, warmth, compassion, sympathy, and concern for the individual. Medicine is now an icy science. Its charm belongs to another age. The dying man can get little comfort from the mechanical doctor."

The psychological implications of microsurgery are as varied as the applications themselves. Those who have lost and then regained a body part are more aware and appreciative of the small things they had taken for granted. But a patient who undergoes any type of surgery, whether performed under the microscope or not, will have adjustments to make. He may have to adapt to a more confined lifestyle, or might find it unnerving to leave the hospital with a different arrangement of parts than when he went in. Every minute of every day, he may gaze at the toe on his hand until enough time has elapsed to incorporate it into his altered body image. Certain psychological adjustments may have negative implications, too. The fact that a woman who has undergone breast reconstruction no longer has an ugly reminder of her mastectomy can also make her forget that she has had cancer and still requires life-long follow-up.

The feats of microsurgery continue to amaze modern science. However, along with its benefits, the psychological effects, ethical concerns, and financial implications microsurgery raises must also be considered when thinking about choosing the procedure.

11
The Future of Microsurgery

Judging from the explosive rate at which new uses are found for microsurgery, the future is bright, indeed. Hospital administrators forecast a steady growth in the number of surgical patients throughout the 1980s, and this will undoubtedly result in many relatively new operations becoming standardized. What we consider innovative today, will be routine tomorrow, only to be replaced by more incredible feats. And this turnover will be swift.

The hypothetical situation with which this book opened—the case of the diver whose arm was deliberately removed, treated, and then replaced—illustrates an important trend in microsurgery known as "bench surgery." Already used in the field of urology, the technique permits extensive work on an organ while it is removed from the body The removal of kidney stones or the repair of accident-induced damage in the kidney, for example, can now be achieved safely and efficiently utilizing this concept of "plug-in" body modules. The kidney is removed from the body, operated on outside the body, and then the repaired kidney is replaced.

This approach will be extended and will be especially important in managing cancer. While tissue remains outside the body, powerful drugs can be administered that would ordinarily be unacceptable to the rest of the body. Studies have shown that a leg could remain in the amputated state for as long as two or three days if properly cooled and preserved. Increasing the length of time that a part remains detached from its owner, however, decreases the function that the part can be expected to regain after it is reattached. Therefore treatment should be completed as rapidly as possible.

Microsurgery is still a young science, and refinement of its techniques can be reasonably assured. One of the most annoying problems that surgeons now face is the tedious stitching of two blood vessels together, only to find when the clamps are removed that blood passage is blocked. A method to check the free opening in the vessel during the operation itself would be welcome in every operating room. Better nerve reconnections are still needed, and this will be an area of much work in the future. Surgeons soon hope to be able to replace children's nerves, defective since birth, with those from other parts of the body.

The correction of other birth defects will become more common. Babies born without fingers may soon have their toes moved to the site. "While this is not a procedure to be carried out willy-nilly, it raises hopes that we can do something for the sizable numbers of infants who are born without fingers," predicts Dr. Richard J. Smith of the Harvard Medical School.

For the immediate future, we can expect to see a further

subspecialization of microsurgical expertise. Just as we have pediatricians whose practice is limited to children, we will soon see pediatric surgeons. An area that holds exciting possibilities is that of performing microsurgery on the unborn. Currently when a mother receives news that the fetus she carries has a serious abnormality which may result in a birth defect, she decides whether or not an abortion might be wise. Soon she may have the additional option of surgical treatment within the uterus through advanced optics and tools.

One of the limits to transplanting parts from other people has been the body's rejection of foreign cells. Once scientists solve this problem, microsurgery can be used to replace any number of body parts. A spare parts bank of tissue from cadavers could be maintained, and drawn from as needed.

Cloning, the creation of an entirely whole organ or tissue from a single cell, may one day be an integral part of microsurgical replacements. Suppose an arm is badly crushed in an accident, and the damage is too extensive for repair. A cell, which contains a complete set of coded genetic instructions within its walls, might be removed and cultured in the laboratory. Soon, a new arm has grown and is ready to replace the original.

Will a robot ever perform an operation on a human being? The idea is not as ludicrous as it sounds. As some motions become too delicate for the surgeon to perform, and instrument capability becomes increasingly sophisticated, designers are creating devices that translate actions into more controlled, mechanized manipulations. The microsurgeon may one day sit back and monitor computer-directed instruments just as NASA workers monitor space-shuttle flights.

Whichever paths microsurgery takes, we can be sure that its future holds many new wonders.

Further Information

HEART AND BLOOD VESSEL DISEASES:

American Heart Association
National Office
7320 Greenville Avenue
Dallas, Tx. 75231
(214) 750-5300
(Information is also available from state and local offices. Check your telephone directory.)

National Heart, Lung, and Blood Vessel Institute
Public Inquiries Office
Room 4A21, Building 31
National Institutes of Health
Bethesda, Md. 20205
(301) 496-4236

Consumer Information Center
Pueblo, Co. 81009
(303) 544-5227, ext. 370

KIDNEY DISEASES AND DONOR PROGRAMS:

National Kidney Foundation
2 Park Avenue
New York, N.Y. 10016
(212) 889-2210
*(Information is also available from state and regional offices.
Check your telephone directory. The Kidney Foundation is a
good source of information about transplantation and organ
donation programs.)*

Living Bank
P.O. Box 6725
Houston, Tx. 77005
(713) 528-2971
*Many states now have arrangements that allow you to register as
an organ donor when you renew your driver's license. Contact
the Department of Motor Vehicles in your state.*

STROKES:

Stroke Club International
805 12th Street
Galveston, Tx. 77550
(713) 762-1022

BIRTH DEFECTS:

National Foundation/March of Dimes
1275 Mamaroneck Avenue
White Plains, N.Y. 10605
(914) 428-7100

Spina Bifida Association of America
343 S. Dearborn Avenue, Suite 319
Chicago, Il. 60604
(312) 663-1562

BRAIN TUMORS:

Association for Brain Tumor Research
6232 N. Pulaski Road, Suite 400
Chicago, Il. 60646
(312) 286-5571

EYE:

National Eye Institute
9000 Rockville Pike
Bethesda, Md. 20014
(301) 496-4000

National Society to Prevent Blindness
79 Madison Avenue
New York, N.Y. 10016
(212) 684-3505

Better Vision Institute
230 Park Avenue
New York, N.Y. 10017
(212) 682-1731

EAR:

Ear Research Institute
256 South Lake Street
Los Angeles, Ca. 90057
(213) 483-4431

DIABETES:

American Diabetes Association
National Offices
600 5th Avenue
New York, N.Y. 10020
(212) 541-4310
(Information is also available from state and regional offices.
Check your telephone directory.)

National Diabetes Information Clearinghouse
805 15 Street, N.W.
Suite 500
Washington, D.C. 20005
(202) 638-7620

FERTILITY AND STERILIZATION:

American Fertility Society
1608 13th Avenue, S., Suite 101
Birmingham, Al. 35205
(205) 933-7222

Association for Voluntary Sterilization
708 Third Avenue
New York, N.Y. 10017
(212) 986-3880

CANCER AND RECONSTRUCTIVE SURGERY:

American Cancer Society
National Headquarters
777 Third Avenue
New York, N.Y. 10017
(212) 371-2900
(Information is also available from state and regional chapter
offices. Check your telephone directory.)

National Cancer Institute
National Institutes of Health
Office of Cancer Communication
Building 31, Room 10A18
Bethesda, Md. 20205
(301) 496-4000
Tollfree hotline (800) 638-6694
(Information is also available from regional information centers. Check your telephone directory under Cancer Information Service.)

American Society of Plastic and Reconstructive Surgeons
29 East Madison Street, Suite 800
Chicago, Il. 60602
(312) 641-0935

AFTER—Ask a Friend to Explain Reconstruction
99 Park Avenue
New York, N.Y. 10016
(212) 986-9099
(This is an organization which provides personal contact with women who have undergone breast reconstruction.)

Bibliography

Altman, Lawrence K., M.D. "Brady's Recovery: Doctors Describe Dramatic Sequence of Lucky Moments." *The New York Times*, May 12, 1981.

Altman, Lawrence K., M.D. "The Doctor's World: Leeches Still Have Their Medical Uses." *The New York Times*, February 17, 1981.

Altman, Lawrence K., M.D. "Eye Surgery Sparks Major Controversy." *The New York Times*, July 29, 1980.

Arehart-Treichel, Joan. "Microsurgery." *Science News*, April 7, 1979, p. 237.

Banttari, Richard. "Gosier Hopeful After Finger Surgery." *Schenectady Gazette*, October 31, 1980.

Banttari, Richard. "3 of 4 Severed Fingers Are Reattached." *Schenectady Gazette*, October 22, 1980.

Breast Reconstruction Following Mastectomy for Cancer. Public Education Committee, American Society of

Plastic and Reconstructive Surgeons, Inc. Chicago: 1979.

Brennan, Eileen. "Medics: The Disorder Men Won't Talk About—Impotence—Is Being Helped By Unusual Bypass Surgery." *People*, November 24, 1980, pp. 51–52.

Chilnick, Larry. "New Computerized System Held Able to Improve Intraocular Microsurgery." *Medical Tribune*, December 3, 1980.

Chipkin, Harvey. "Revascularization: A New Way to Help Stroke Victims." *Family Health*, November-December 1980, p. 9

Christopher, Rita and Larry Black. "Dr. Gulliver's Adventures in Lilliput." *Maclean's*, July 9, 1979, p. 37.

Clark, Matt and Dan Shapiro. "The Delicate Art of Microsurgery." *Newsweek*, June 25, 1979, pp. 97–99.

Colligan, Douglas. "Artificial Organs: Replacing the Irreplaceable." *New York*, October 22, 1979, pp. 53–61.

Colman, Gerald, M.D. "Surgery—Breakthrough." *The Keys*. Albany: St. Peter's Hospital, Summer 1980, pp. 1–2.

"Creative Microsurgeon." *MD Medical Newsmagazine*, June 1980, pp. 47–48.

Dana, Maureen McTague. "Albany Doctors Eye a Myopia 'Miracle.' " *The Knickerbocker News*, September 5, 1980.

"Doctor's Deathbed Plea: 'Let Ill Choose How to Die.' " *The Knickerbocker News*, October 10, 1980.

Dzinanka, Steve. "Nearsighted Brother, Sister Try New Surgical Correction." *Schenectady Gazette*, December 24, 1980.

Englebardt, Stanley L. "The Marvels of Microsurgery." *The Atlantic Monthly*, February 1980, pp. 68–73.

Fein, Jack M. "Microvascular Surgery for Stroke." *Scientific American*, April 1978, pp. 58–67.

Fortino, Denise. "Microsurgery: Reversing Sterilization." *Harper's Bazaar*, December 1979, p. 173.

Freese, Arthur S. "Microsurgery: Medicine's Big New Hope." *Science Digest*, May 1969, pp. 7–11.

Henahan, John F. "Surgery Under a Microscope: Reassembling Our Fragile Life Lines." *Science Digest*, October 1978, pp. 53–57.

Hyland, Kevin. "Microsurgery: A Small Wonder." *Syracuse Herald-American*, January 27, 1980.

Knox, Richard A. "Medical Progress in 1980 Shares Limelight with Biocommercialism." *Clearwater Sun*, December 28, 1980.

"Microsurgery." *MD Medical Newsmagazine*, June 1980, pp. 71–81.

"Microsurgery for Pituitary Tumors." *Science News*, July 30, 1977, p. 71.

"Microsurgery for Strokes and Visual Disorders." *Science News*, February 3, 1979, p. 69.

"Microsurgery—New Infertility Breakthrough." *USA Today*, February, 1980, pp. 10–11.

Nolen, William A., M.D. " 'Invisible' Operations That Save Lives." *McCall's*, September 1980, p. 88.

"Now: TV Microscope for Surgery." *Popular Mechanics*, February 1975, p. 136.

Plastic and Reconstructive Surgery. The American Society of Plastic and Reconstructive Surgeons, Inc. Chicago: 1979.

"Preventing Strokes." *Newsweek*, January 31, 1977, p. 79.

"Replacement Surgery Brings Light to Cataract Victims." *Schenectady Gazette*, June 23, 1980.

Retzlaff, Eric. "Microsurgery Provides New Hope for Infertile." *Schenectady Gazette*, January 19, 1981.

Russell, Cristine. "Chinese Medicine: Old & New." *Science News*, October 27, 1979, pp. 292–293.

Schildkraut, Midge Lasky. "The Miracles of Microsurgery." *Good Housekeeping*, February 1980, pp. 261–262.

Schmeck, Harold M., Jr. "Therapy in the Womb Rescues Unborn Lives." *The New York Times*, May 25, 1981.

"Severed Arms Restored, Miner Glad He's Able to Shave." *Schenectady Gazette*, April 21, 1980.

Siegal, Robert S. "Medics: Dr. Harold Kleinert Reattaches Severed Limbs Through the Fine Art of Microsurgery." *People*, July 31, 1978, pp. 43–45.

Silber, Sherman. *Microsurgery*. Baltimore: Williams & Wilkins, 1979.

Sullivan, Walter. "Chinese Cite Gains in Limb Attachment." *The New York Times*, January 7, 1981.

Thomas, Sally Galbraith and Marilyn Mann Yates. "Breast Reconstruction After Mastectomy." *American Journal of Nursing*, September 1977, pp. 1438–1442.

"Tiny Lenses That Let You See Again." *50 Plus*, April 1981, p. 22.

"A Tragic Choice for Parents." *The Knickerbocker News*, March 20, 1981.

"U.S. Doctors Study Techniques of Microsurgery with Chinese." *Schenectady Gazette*, April 20, 1981.

Wasco, Dr. James. *Not for Doctors Only*. Reading, Massachusetts: Addison-Wesley Publishing Company, Inc., 1980.

Williams, Gurney, III. "Lifesaving Surgery—Under a Lens." *Popular Mechanics*, March 1979, pp. 92–95.

Wylie, Evan McLeod. "Microsurgery: The New Hope for Men and Women Who Were Surgically Sterilized and Now Want to Have Babies." *Good Housekeeping*, September 1978, pp. 108–117.

Index